Mathematics
GCSE

Book 2

Oxford University Press, Walton Street, Oxford OX2 6DP

Oxford New York Toronto
Delhi Bombay Calcutta Madras Karachi
Petaling Jaya Singapore Hong Kong Tokyo
Nairobi Dar es Salaam Cape Town
Melbourne Auckland

and associated companies in
Beirut Berlin Ibadan Nicosia

Oxford is a trade mark of Oxford University Press

© Oxford University Press 1987

ISBN 0 19 914246 7

First published 1987

Cartoons by David Simonds and Peter Joyce

Typeset by Katerprint Typesetting Services, Oxford
Printed and bound in Great Britain by
William Clowes Limited, Beccles and London

PREFACE

This two-book course has been written for the majority of secondary school pupils attempting the GCSE in mathematics and can be used in the two to three years leading to the examination. It provides practice in all the topics of Lists 1 and 2 of the National Criteria and of the syllabuses of the examining groups at this level.

The many practice questions are arranged in exercises which are graded to match the abilities of pupils in a given class. Because the books cover a wide range of abilities, it is not expected that all the questions in every exercise will be attempted. It is the author's experience that pupils who find mathematics difficult will derive much pleasure and satisfaction from the subject in doing questions that help to build up their confidence. If the work can be covered systematically, an appreciation of the purpose and the power of the subject can be developed, leading to a realisation of the use of mathematics in everyday practical situations and in future employment.

An important part of each book is to be found in the 'Think about it' sections. In these, the projects form a lively platform for investigational work and discussion which can be extended at the discretion of the teacher and used as a basis for assessment. They are intended to develop the pupil's ability to reason logically, to appreciate patterns and relationships and to stimulate powers of creative imagination. The exercises inserted between these projects aim to widen the perceptive abilities of the pupil.

Each book also includes a section of mental arithmetic tests in which questions are read out to the class with books closed. A competitive element can be enjoyed here with the text later used for pupils to check their errors. The numerical answers to both books are provided in one separate answer book.

The author wishes to record his thanks to Micheline Dubois, Philip Cutts and all his colleagues at school for all their help. Thanks are also due to the following examination boards for kindly allowing the use of questions in Book 2 from their specimen mathematics papers.

London and East Anglian Group for GCSE [L]
Midland Examining Group [M]
Northern Examining Association [N]
Southern Examining Group [S]
Welsh Joint Education Committee [W]

CONTENTS

Part 1

1.1 ARITHMETIC WITHOUT A CALCULATOR

Addition and subtraction

Exercise 1

Work out, without a calculator.

1. 215 + 68
2. 322 + 638
3. 39 + 2184
4. 62 + 3906
5. 713 + 5607
6. 178 + 6058
7. 23 + 615 + 237
8. 47 + 205 + 411
9. 27 + 24 078
10. 6518 + 6174
11. 274 − 62
12. 953 − 22
13. 858 − 74
14. 953 − 147
15. 382 − 94
16. 410 − 65
17. 715 − 206
18. 8926 − 1936
19. 2500 − 2488
20. 6163 − 4185

21. Two hundred and six add three hundred and seventeen.
22. Five hundred and eleven add nine hundred and twenty-eight.
23. Fifteen thousand and twenty add four thousand, two hundred and forty-one.
24. Twenty thousand, six hundred and ten add three hundred and ninety-seven.
25. Two hundred and ten thousand, three hundred add twenty-eight thousand eight hundred.
26. Four hundred and eight take away two hundred and eleven.
27. Seven hundred and eighty take away three hundred and thirty-one.
28. Five thousand and nine take away four hundred.
29. Six thousand, two hundred and seven take away three hundred and twelve.
30. Seven thousand and sixteen take away four thousand, two hundred and two.

Exercise 2

Work out, without a calculator.

1. 5.6 + 8.21	**2.** 3.04 + 5.6
3. 9.5 + 11.4	**4.** 6.34 + 7.08
5. 6 + 2.4	**6.** 8 + 2.35
7. 3.09 + 7	**8.** 7.2 + 11.8
9. 3.1 + 0.6 + 3.7	**10.** 8.5 + 11.7 + 0.26
11. 8 + 11.7 + 0.34	**12.** 2.75 + 25
13. 21.65 + 2.45	**14.** 18 + 2.6 + 11
15. 5.065 + 2.994	**16.** 3.087 + 2.009
17. 3.64 − 2.12	**18.** 8.88 − 1.65
19. 9.62 − 1.51	**20.** 9.85 − 7.17
21. 3.84 − 0.92	**22.** 11.2 − 0.3
23. 8.9 − 7	**24.** 13.6 − 7
25. 13.09 − 9	**26.** 8 − 2.5
27. 11 − 7.4	**28.** 23 − 15.5
29. 9.9 − 8.16	**30.** 8.2 − 1.16
31. 9 − 3.6	**32.** 100 − 99.25
33. 3.07 − 0.09	**34.** 13 − 7.6
35. 27.8 − 19	**36.** 258.1 − 17.3
37. 4.825 − 1.666	**38.** 8.57 − 1.99
39. 8 − 3.63	**40.** 19 − 12.73

Multiplication and division

Exercise 3

Work out, without a calculator.

1. 27 × 3	**2.** 82 × 2
3. 33 × 5	**4.** 49 × 4
5. 82 × 3	**6.** 232 × 5
7. 216 × 6	**8.** 323 × 7
9. 305 × 7	**10.** 411 × 8
11. 201 × 22	**12.** 314 × 24
13. 62 × 31	**14.** 84 × 35
15. 712 × 35	**16.** 818 × 62
17. 714 × 27	**18.** 923 × 83
19. 607 × 91	**20.** 425 × 216
21. 316 × 324	**22.** 718 × 416
23. 509 × 207	**24.** 306 × 333

Exercise 4

Work out, without a calculator.

1. 693 ÷ 3	**2.** 1260 ÷ 4
3. 1180 ÷ 5	**4.** 764 ÷ 2
5. 1668 ÷ 4	**6.** 3972 ÷ 6
7. 1056 ÷ 3	**8.** 4795 ÷ 7
9. 12 852 ÷ 6	**10.** 5376 ÷ 8
11. 22 155 ÷ 7	**12.** 1254 ÷ 6

13. 4856 ÷ 8	**14.** 1570 ÷ 5
15. 3069 ÷ 9	**16.** 10 696 ÷ 4
17. 4830 ÷ 6	**18.** 28 269 ÷ 9
19. 1660 ÷ 5	**20.** 24 054 ÷ 6
21. 2948 ÷ 11	**22.** 28 777 ÷ 7
23. 4424 ÷ 7	**24.** 96 084 ÷ 12
25. 37 480 ÷ 8	**26.** 26 609 ÷ 11
27. 34 353 ÷ 9	**28.** 19 341 ÷ 7
29. 168 945 ÷ 7	**30.** 34 435 ÷ 5
31. 10.68 ÷ 4	**32.** 15.3 ÷ 5
33. 20.484 ÷ 6	**34.** 22.728 ÷ 8
35. 406.3 ÷ 5	**36.** 10.398 ÷ 3
37. 37.76 ÷ 8	**38.** 6.732 ÷ 9
39. 57.89 ÷ 7	**40.** 15.035 ÷ 5

Multiplying and dividing with decimals

Work out (a) 1.7×0.6 (b) 3.6×0.41
            (c) $3.25 \div 0.4$ (d) $8.6 \div 0.02$

(a) Ignore the decimal points and work
    out 17 × 6
        $17 \times 6 = 102$
        $\therefore 1.7 \times 0.6 = \mathbf{1.02}$
(b) $36 \times 41 = 1476$
        $\therefore 3.6 \times 0.41 = \mathbf{1.476}$
(c) $3.25 \div 0.4 = 32.5 \div 4$
        $= \mathbf{8.125}$
(d) $8.6 \div 0.02 = 860 \div 2$
        $= \mathbf{430}$.

Exercise 5

Work out, without a calculator.

1. 3.2 × 0.5	**2.** 27.4 × 0.4
3. 4.1 × 0.7	**4.** 3.6 × 0.6
5. 5.5 × 0.8	**6.** 8.01 × 0.9
7. 3.6 × 1.2	**8.** 5.6 × 0.06
9. 81.2 × 0.05	**10.** 74 × 3.1
11. 63.2 × 0.001	**12.** 120 × 0.11
13. 58 × 0.02	**14.** 635 × 0.6
15. 63 × 0.04	**16.** 0.74 × 0.15
17. 0.63 × 0.74	**18.** 5.62 × 0.07
19. 5.27 × 0.41	**20.** 99 × 0.007
21. 1.448 ÷ 0.4	**22.** 0.435 ÷ 0.3
23. 4.12 ÷ 0.5	**24.** 0.02856 ÷ 0.04
25. 0.2262 ÷ 0.06	**26.** 0.5782 ÷ 0.07
27. 0.01323 ÷ 0.09	**28.** 0.000438 ÷ 0.006
29. 5.82 ÷ 0.1	**30.** 0.1918 ÷ 0.007
31. 64.86 ÷ 0.3	**32.** 4.114 ÷ 0.11
33. 62.244 ÷ 0.12	**34.** 1.9584 ÷ 0.008

The next exercise contains a mixture of
questions on addition, subtraction,
multiplication and division.

Exercise 6

Work out, without a calculator.

1. 0.24 + 3.686	**2.** 5.7 − 1.45	**13.** 2.9 + 12	**14.** 0.41 ÷ 100
3. 0.62 × 0.3	**4.** 36.2 × 1.1	**15.** 0.09 − 0.076	**16.** 2184 + 5688
5. 8.72 ÷ 0.4	**6.** 0.0062 ÷ 0.02	**17.** 56.2 ÷ 0.001	**18.** 6324 − 5686
7. 18.5 − 9.6	**8.** 11 + 3.74	**19.** 0.5 × 0.6	**20.** 516 ÷ 10 000
9. 2.6 ÷ 0.05	**10.** 8 − 1.4	**21.** 45.1 − 8.6	**22.** 0.6 × 100
11. 12.1 × 0.7	**12.** 2.6 × 1000	**23.** 0.7 + 1.35 + 0.09	**24.** 99.9 − 85.95
		25. 5.6 + 2.9 − 1.84	**26.** 5.6 ÷ 0.005
		27. 0.82 + 1.36 − 0.95	**28.** 2.45 × 1.2
		29. 0.0043 × 10 000	**30.** 2583 ÷ 7
		31. 9.2 − 8.3 − 0.06	**32.** 7 − 0.33
		33. 0.21 ÷ 100	**34.** 2856 ÷ 8
		35. 2.41 × 3.5	**36.** 1.8 + 19.6 − 15.55
		37. 0.621 × 0.31	**38.** 5346 ÷ 11

Making a profit

A shopkeeper buys potatoes at a wholesale price of £180 per tonne
and sells them at a retail price of 22p per kg. How much profit does he
make on one kilogram of potatoes?

He pays £180 for 1000 kg of potatoes.

∴   He pays £[180 ÷ 1000] for 1 kg of potatoes.

i.e.   He pays 18p for 1 kg

He sells at 22p per kg.

∴   Profit = 4p per kg.

Exercise 7

Find the profit in each case.

	Commodity	Retail price	Wholesale price	Profit
1.	cans of drink	15p each	£11 per 100	profit per can?
2.	rulers	24p each	£130 per 1000	profit per ruler?
3.	birthday cards	22p each	£13 per 100	profit per card?
4.	soup	27p per can	£8.50 for 50 cans	profit per can?
5.	newspapers	22p each	£36 for 200	profit per paper?
6.	box of matches	37p each	£15.20 for 80	profit per box?
7.	potatoes	22p per kg	£160 per tonne	profit per kg?
8.	carrots	38p per kg	£250 per tonne	profit per kg?
9.	T-shirts	£4.95 each	£38.40 per dozen	profit per T-shirt?
10.	eggs	96p per dozen	£50 per 1000	profit per dozen?
11.	oranges	5 for 30p	£14 for 400	profit per orange?
12.	car tyres	£19.50 each	£2450 for 200	profit per tyre?
13.	wine	55p for 100 ml	£40 for 10 litres	profit per 100 ml?
14.	sand	16p per kg	£110 per tonne	profit per kg?
15.	wire	23p per m	£700 for 10 km	profit per m?
16.	cheese	£2.64 per kg	£87.50 for 50 kg	profit per kg?
17.	copper tube	46p per m	£160 for 500 m	profit per m?
18.	apples	9p each	£10.08 per gross	profit per apple?
19.	carpet	£6.80 per m^2	£1600 for 500 m^2	profit per m^2?
20.	tin of soup	33p per tin	£72 for 400 tins	profit per tin?

1.2 FRACTIONS

Exercise 8

Write the fractions in their simplest form.

1. $\frac{6}{9}$ 2. $\frac{12}{16}$ 3. $\frac{18}{20}$ 4. $\frac{24}{30}$

5. $\frac{12}{18}$ 6. $\frac{8}{12}$ 7. $\frac{9}{15}$ 8. $\frac{6}{24}$

9. $\frac{6}{18}$ 10. $\frac{4}{18}$ 11. $\frac{20}{60}$ 12. $\frac{40}{120}$

13. $\frac{54}{81}$ 14. $\frac{28}{36}$ 15. $\frac{18}{30}$ 16. $\frac{56}{64}$

17. $\frac{72}{162}$ 18. $\frac{132}{144}$ 19. $\frac{35}{45}$ 20. $\frac{55}{60}$

21. $\frac{30}{72}$ 22. $\frac{42}{60}$ 23. $\frac{44}{121}$ 24. $\frac{77}{132}$

25. $\frac{24}{40}$ 26. $\frac{56}{60}$ 27. $\frac{64}{120}$ 28. $\frac{9}{63}$

29. $\frac{45}{100}$ 30. $\frac{20}{500}$ 31. $\frac{20}{5000}$ 32. $\frac{21}{49}$

33. $\frac{70}{560}$ 34. $\frac{36}{216}$ 35. $\frac{121}{440}$ 36. $\frac{25}{400}$

37. $\frac{34}{51}$ 38. $\frac{6}{15}$ 39. $\frac{40}{140}$ 40. $\frac{81}{540}$

41. $\frac{56}{840}$ 42. $\frac{64}{880}$ 43. $\frac{7}{630}$ 44. $\frac{15}{75}$

45. $\frac{52}{65}$ 46. $\frac{64}{72}$ 47. $\frac{21}{35}$ 48. $\frac{96}{108}$

49. $\frac{650}{1040}$ 50. $\frac{2800}{3600}$ 51. $\frac{105}{400}$ 52. $\frac{225}{500}$

Exercise 9

Write as mixed numbers in their simplest form.

1. $\frac{7}{4}$ 2. $\frac{8}{5}$ 3. $\frac{9}{4}$ 4. $\frac{11}{4}$

5. $\frac{8}{3}$ 6. $\frac{5}{2}$ 7. $\frac{5}{3}$ 8. $\frac{6}{5}$

9. $\frac{11}{4}$ 10. $\frac{7}{3}$ 11. $\frac{11}{6}$ 12. $\frac{12}{5}$

13. $\frac{13}{6}$ 14. $\frac{7}{2}$ 15. $\frac{9}{7}$ 16. $\frac{18}{5}$

17. $\frac{21}{5}$ 18. $\frac{10}{3}$ 19. $\frac{12}{7}$ 20. $\frac{60}{11}$

21. $\frac{70}{12}$ 22. $\frac{24}{7}$ 23. $\frac{30}{8}$ 24. $\frac{40}{12}$

25. $\frac{53}{9}$ 26. $\frac{100}{9}$ 27. $\frac{41}{5}$ 28. $\frac{73}{10}$

29. $\frac{38}{9}$ 30. $\frac{97}{11}$ 31. $\frac{100}{11}$ 32. $\frac{20}{7}$

33. $\frac{52}{7}$ 34. $\frac{84}{10}$ 35. $\frac{65}{16}$ 36. $\frac{52}{8}$

37. $\frac{38}{7}$ 38. $\frac{25}{17}$ 39. $\frac{30}{13}$ 40. $\frac{45}{8}$

41. $\frac{33}{9}$ 42. $\frac{22}{3}$ 43. $\frac{200}{12}$ 44. $\frac{75}{50}$

45. $\frac{26}{9}$ 46. $\frac{200}{55}$ 47. $\frac{1000}{400}$ 48. $\frac{250}{40}$

49. $\frac{3}{2}$ 50. $\frac{58}{12}$ 51. $\frac{35}{11}$ 52. $\frac{205}{210}$

Adding and subtracting fractions

(a) $\frac{1}{2} + \frac{5}{8}$

$= \frac{4}{8} + \frac{5}{8}$

$= \frac{9}{8}$

$= 1\frac{1}{8}$

(b) $\frac{3}{5} - \frac{1}{4}$

$= \frac{12}{20} - \frac{5}{20}$

$= \frac{7}{20}$

Exercise 10

Work out.

1. $\frac{1}{4} + \frac{3}{8}$ 2. $\frac{3}{4} + \frac{1}{2}$ 3. $\frac{1}{8} + \frac{3}{4}$

4. $\frac{1}{2} + \frac{7}{8}$ 5. $\frac{3}{4} - \frac{1}{8}$ 6. $\frac{5}{8} - \frac{1}{4}$

7. $\frac{7}{8} + \frac{1}{16}$ 8. $\frac{5}{16} + \frac{1}{4}$ 9. $\frac{3}{8} - \frac{3}{16}$

10. $\frac{7}{8} + \frac{5}{16}$ 11. $\frac{1}{2} + \frac{7}{16}$ 12. $\frac{3}{4} - \frac{9}{16}$

13. $\frac{3}{4} - \frac{1}{16}$ 14. $\frac{11}{16} - \frac{1}{4}$ 15. $\frac{7}{8} + \frac{13}{16}$

16. $\frac{2}{3} + \frac{1}{4}$ 17. $\frac{3}{5} + \frac{1}{2}$ 18. $\frac{4}{5} + \frac{1}{4}$

19. $\frac{3}{5} + \frac{2}{3}$ 20. $\frac{5}{6} + \frac{1}{2}$ 21. $\frac{3}{4} + \frac{4}{5}$

22. $\frac{5}{6} + \frac{1}{2}$ 23. $\frac{5}{7} + \frac{1}{4}$ 24. $\frac{2}{5} - \frac{1}{3}$

25. $\frac{7}{8} - \frac{2}{3}$ 26. $\frac{5}{8} - \frac{1}{5}$ 27. $\frac{6}{7} - \frac{1}{3}$

28. $\frac{3}{8} - \frac{1}{10}$ 29. $\frac{4}{9} - \frac{1}{4}$ 30. $\frac{5}{11} - \frac{1}{4}$

Multiplying and dividing fractions

(a) $\frac{5}{6} \times \frac{5}{7} = \frac{25}{42}$ (b) $\frac{2}{3} \times \frac{5}{7} = \frac{10}{21}$

(c) $\frac{4}{5} \div \frac{3}{4} = \frac{4}{5} \times \frac{4}{3} = \frac{16}{15} = 1\frac{1}{15}$

Exercise 11

Work out and simplify where possible.

1. $\frac{2}{3} \times \frac{1}{5}$ 2. $\frac{3}{4} \times \frac{5}{7}$ 3. $\frac{4}{5} \times \frac{2}{3}$

4. $\frac{5}{6} \times \frac{5}{7}$ 5. $\frac{5}{9} \times \frac{2}{3}$ 6. $\frac{4}{11} \times \frac{5}{6}$

7. $\frac{7}{8} \times \frac{3}{4}$ 8. $\frac{8}{9} \times \frac{3}{4}$ 9. $\frac{7}{10} \times \frac{1}{2}$

10. $\frac{4}{7} \times \frac{14}{15}$ 11. $\frac{3}{5} \times \frac{7}{8}$ 12. $\frac{5}{8} \times \frac{1}{2}$

13. $\frac{3}{2} \times \frac{1}{4}$ 14. $\frac{5}{4} \times \frac{1}{3}$ 15. $\frac{7}{3} \times \frac{1}{4}$

16. $\frac{3}{4} \div \frac{1}{2}$ 17. $\frac{3}{5} \div \frac{2}{3}$ 18. $\frac{5}{6} \div \frac{1}{4}$

19. $\frac{2}{3} \div \frac{3}{4}$ 20. $\frac{5}{6} \div \frac{3}{4}$ 21. $\frac{5}{7} \div \frac{3}{4}$

22. $\frac{1}{3} \div \frac{1}{10}$ 23. $\frac{1}{8} \div \frac{3}{4}$ 24. $\frac{5}{8} \div \frac{1}{2}$

25. $2\frac{1}{2} \times \frac{1}{3}$ 26. $3\frac{1}{2} \times \frac{1}{4}$ 27. $1\frac{1}{4} \times \frac{1}{5}$

28. $2\frac{1}{4} \times \frac{1}{2}$ 29. $3\frac{1}{5} \times \frac{2}{3}$ 30. $2\frac{1}{5} \times \frac{1}{4}$

31. $1\frac{1}{4} \div 2$ 32. $3\frac{1}{2} \div 3$ 33. $2\frac{3}{4} \div 5$

34. $3\frac{1}{10} \div \frac{1}{2}$ 35. $5\frac{1}{4} \times \frac{1}{7}$ 36. $3\frac{2}{9} \div \frac{1}{3}$

Exercise 12

Work out and simplify where possible.

1. $\frac{1}{3} + \frac{1}{2}$ 2. $\frac{1}{3} \times \frac{1}{2}$ 3. $\frac{1}{3} \div \frac{1}{2}$

4. $\frac{3}{4} - \frac{1}{3}$ 5. $\frac{3}{4} \times \frac{1}{3}$ 6. $\frac{3}{4} \div \frac{1}{3}$

7. $\frac{2}{5} + \frac{1}{2}$ 8. $\frac{2}{5} \times \frac{1}{2}$ 9. $\frac{2}{5} \div \frac{1}{2}$

10. $\frac{3}{7} + \frac{1}{2}$ 11. $\frac{3}{7} \times \frac{1}{2}$ 12. $\frac{3}{7} \div \frac{1}{2}$

13. $\frac{5}{8} - \frac{1}{4}$ 14. $\frac{5}{8} \times \frac{1}{4}$ 15. $\frac{5}{8} \div \frac{1}{4}$

16. $\frac{1}{6} + \frac{4}{5}$ 17. $\frac{1}{6} \times \frac{4}{5}$ 18. $\frac{1}{6} \div \frac{4}{5}$

19. $\frac{3}{7} + \frac{1}{3}$ 20. $\frac{3}{7} \times \frac{1}{3}$ 21. $\frac{3}{7} \div \frac{1}{3}$

22. $\frac{4}{5} - \frac{1}{4}$ 23. $\frac{4}{5} \times \frac{1}{4}$ 24. $\frac{4}{5} \div \frac{1}{4}$

25. $\frac{2}{3} - \frac{1}{8}$ 26. $\frac{2}{3} \times \frac{1}{8}$ 27. $\frac{2}{3} \div \frac{1}{8}$

28. $\frac{5}{9} + \frac{1}{4}$ 29. $\frac{5}{9} \times \frac{1}{4}$ 30. $\frac{5}{9} \div \frac{1}{4}$

31. $2\frac{1}{2} - \frac{1}{4}$ 32. $2\frac{1}{2} \times \frac{1}{4}$ 33. $2\frac{1}{2} \div \frac{1}{4}$

34. $3\frac{3}{4} - \frac{2}{3}$ 35. $3\frac{3}{4} \times \frac{2}{3}$ 36. $3\frac{3}{4} \div \frac{2}{3}$

37. $\dfrac{\frac{1}{2} + \frac{1}{5}}{\frac{1}{2} - \frac{1}{5}}$

38. $\dfrac{\frac{3}{4} - \frac{1}{3}}{\frac{3}{4} + \frac{1}{3}}$

39. $\dfrac{2\frac{1}{4} \times \frac{4}{5}}{\frac{3}{5} - \frac{1}{2}}$

40. $\dfrac{3\frac{1}{2} \times 2\frac{2}{3}}{\frac{1}{2} + 1\frac{1}{18}}$

Changing fractions to decimals

(a) $\frac{5}{8}$

$$\begin{array}{r} 0.625 \\ 8\overline{)5.000} \end{array}$$

$\frac{5}{8} = 0.625$

(b) $\frac{5}{6}$

$$\begin{array}{r} 0.8333... \\ 6\overline{)5.0000} \end{array}$$

$\frac{5}{6} = 0.8\dot{3}$

Exercise 13

Change the fractions to decimals.

1. $\frac{3}{4}$ 2. $\frac{1}{2}$ 3. $\frac{3}{8}$ 4. $\frac{2}{5}$

5. $\frac{7}{8}$ 6. $\frac{1}{4}$ 7. $\frac{4}{5}$ 8. $\frac{3}{10}$

9. $\frac{1}{8}$ 10. $\frac{1}{3}$ 11. $\frac{2}{3}$ 12. $\frac{1}{6}$

13. $\frac{4}{9}$ 14. $\frac{5}{9}$ 15. $\frac{7}{100}$ 16. $\frac{11}{100}$

17. $\frac{7}{50}$ 18. $\frac{9}{20}$ 19. $\frac{9}{1000}$ 20. $\frac{17}{1000}$

21. $\frac{3}{50}$ 22. $\frac{1}{9}$ 23. $\frac{5}{12}$ 24. $\frac{11}{12}$

In questions **25** to **36** write the decimal correct to three decimal places.

25. $\frac{5}{7}$ 26. $\frac{2}{7}$ 27. $\frac{4}{11}$ 28. $\frac{8}{9}$

29. $\frac{1}{7}$ 30. $\frac{7}{11}$ 31. $\frac{5}{13}$ 32. $\frac{8}{13}$

33. $\frac{4}{15}$ 34. $\frac{1}{30}$ 35. $\frac{7}{90}$ 36. $\frac{5}{60}$

Number facts

(a) A *prime* number is divisible only by itself and by one.
e.g. 2, 3, 5, 7, 11, 13 . . .

(b) The *multiples* of 12 are 12, 24, 36, 48 . . .

(c) The *factors* of 12 are 1, 2, 3, 4, 6, 12.

(d) Rational and irrational numbers
The *exact* value of a *rational* number can be written down.
e.g. 3, $2\frac{1}{2}$, 5.72, $-3\frac{3}{4}$.
The exact value of an *irrational* number *cannot* be written down.
e.g. π, $\sqrt{2}$, $\sqrt{3}$, $\sqrt{5}$.

Exercise 14

1. Which of the following are prime numbers?
3, 11, 15, 19, 21, 23, 27, 29, 31, 37, 39, 47, 51, 59, 61, 67, 72, 73, 87, 99.

2. Write down the first five multiples of the following numbers:
(a) 4   (b) 6   (c) 10
(d) 11   (e) 20.

3. Write down the first six multiples of 4 and of 6. What are the first two *common* multiples of 4 and 6? [i.e. multiples of both 4 and 6]

4. Write down the first six multiples of 3 and of 5. What is the lowest common multiple of 3 and 5?

5. Write down all the factors of the following:
(a) 6   (b) 9   (c) 10
(d) 15   (e) 24   (f) 32

6. Decide which of the following are rational numbers and which are irrational:
(a) 3.5   (b) 3.153   (c) $\sqrt{7}$
(d) $\frac{1}{3}$ (e) 0.072   (f) $\sqrt{2}$

(g) $\sqrt{4}$ (h) π (i) $\dfrac{\sqrt{3}}{2}$

(j) $\sqrt{100}$ (k) $-2\frac{3}{7}$ (l) $\sqrt{5}$

1.3 PERCENTAGES

Change into percentages:

(a) $\frac{4}{5}$ (b) $\frac{3}{8}$ (c) 16 out of 40.

(a) $\frac{4}{5} \times \frac{100}{1} = \frac{400}{5} = \mathbf{80\%}$

(b) $\frac{3}{8} \times \frac{100}{1} = \frac{300}{8} = \mathbf{37\frac{1}{2}\%}$

(c) 16 out of 40 $= \frac{16}{40}$

$\frac{16}{40} \times \frac{100}{1} = \frac{1600}{40} = \mathbf{40\%}$

Exercise 15

Change into percentages.

1. $\frac{2}{5}$ 2. $\frac{3}{4}$ 3. $\frac{5}{8}$
4. $\frac{7}{100}$ 5. $\frac{12}{50}$ 6. $\frac{7}{20}$
7. $\frac{7}{8}$ 8. $\frac{1}{3}$ 9. $\frac{1}{8}$
10. $\frac{3}{50}$ 11. $\frac{19}{100}$ 12. $\frac{24}{40}$
13. $\frac{64}{80}$ 14. $\frac{17}{25}$ 15. $\frac{13}{1000}$

16. 27 out of 50.
17. 72 out of 80.
18. 3 out of 40.
19. 11 out of 20.
20. 220 out of 1000.

Work out: (a) 22% of £400,
              (b) $8\frac{1}{2}$% of £300.

(a) $\frac{22}{100} \times \frac{400}{1} = £88$

(b) $\frac{8.5}{100} \times 300 = £25.50$

Exercise 16

Work out.

1. 12% of £600   2. 6% of £250
3. 8% of £450   4. 7% of £440
5. 5% of £22   6. 4% of £660
7. 85% of £400   8. 6.5% of £200
9. 29% of £2000   10. 4.5% of £400
11. 62% of $4000   12. 1.4% of $6000
13. 49% of $10 000   14. 25% of 64 m
15. $12\frac{1}{2}$% of 160 kg   16. 80% of 600 km
17. 50% of 0.62 kg   18. $33\frac{1}{3}$% of 327 km
19. 1% of £2   20. 5% of 200 kg

In questions **21** to **40** give the answer correct to the nearest penny.

21. 13% of £2.13   22. 27% of £5.85
23. 11% of £6.27   24. 13% of £6.17
25. 37% of £5.20   26. 15% of £11.23
27. 6.2% of £8.55   28. 31% of £35.04
29. 8.9% of £17.10   30. 6.8% of £16.10
31. 81% of £9.32   32. 15.1% of £7.87
33. 43% of £185   34. 16% of £0.37
35. 1.8% of £2555   36. 4% of £0.65
37. 3.7% of £6.12   38. 78% of £3.17
39. 17% of £1754   40. 23% of £18.05

The next three exercises involve percentages as they are used in everyday life.

Hire purchase

Exercise 17

1. The cash price of an electric cooker is £540. The hire purchase terms are:
   Deposit: 20% of cash price
   Instalments: 24 monthly payments of £20.75
   Calculate (a) the deposit
                 (b) the total monthly instalments
                 (c) the total hire purchase price of the cooker.

2. Steve wished to buy a motor cycle priced at £480. He chose to pay by hire purchase. The terms were 30% deposit with 12 monthly payments of £33.80.
   Calculate (a) the deposit
                 (b) the total of the monthly payments
                 (c) the total hire purchase price of the motor cycle.

3. The cash price of a video recorder is £485. The hire purchase terms are:
   Deposit: 30% of cash price
   Instalments: 18 monthly payments of £23.
   Calculate (a) the deposit
                 (b) the total monthly instalments
                 (c) the total hire purchase price.

4. David wishes to buy a computer priced at £360. He choses to pay by hire purchase the terms for which are 30% deposit and 24 monthly payments of £12.50.
   Calculate (a) the total hire purchase price
                 (b) the difference between the cash price and the hire purchase price.

5. A television set is priced at £320 in two different shops A and B, which offer different hire purchase terms.
   Shop A requires a 20% deposit and 12 monthly instalments of £26.60.
   Shop B requires a 30% deposit and 12 monthly instalments of £23.50.
   Calculate (a) the total hire purchase price in Shop A.
   (b) the total hire purchase price in Shop B.

6. The cash price of a caravan is £3400. The hire purchase terms are 25% deposit and 12 monthly payments. The total hire purchase price is £4090.
   Calculate (a) the deposit
   (b) the difference between the deposit and the total hire purchase price
   (c) the amount of each monthly instalment.

7. The cash price of a car is £840. The hire purchase terms are $33\frac{1}{3}$% deposit and 24 monthly payments. The total hire purchase price is £980.80.
   Calculate (a) the deposit
   (b) the total of the 24 monthly instalments.
   (c) the amount of each monthly instalment.

8. A man may obtain a TV set from a shop in three different ways:
   (i) He can buy the set for £285 cash.
   (ii) He can pay a deposit of 20% of £285 followed by 24 monthly instalments of £11.60.
   (iii) He can rent the set paying £3 a week for the first year and £2.70 a week for the next two years. Calculate
   (a) the total hire purchase price.
   (b) the cost of renting the set for 3 years.

9. A car costs £1800. Mr Wilson pays by taking out a bank loan for £1800. The bank makes a charge of 22% of the loan. The bank loan plus interest has to be repaid by 18 equal monthly payments. Calculate
   (a) the interest charged
   (b) the total of the loan plus interest
   (c) the amount of each monthly payment.

10.

(a) The cooker can be bought on hire purchase by paying a deposit of 35% and 36 monthly payments of £11.40. How much is
   (i) the deposit
   (ii) the total of the monthly payments
   (iii) the total hire purchase price?
(b) The cooker can also be bought using a bank loan for £460. The bank makes a charge of 20% of the loan and requires the loan plus interest to be repaid by 24 equal monthly payments. Calculate
   (i) the interest charged
   (ii) the total cost by this method
   (iii) the amount of each monthly payment.

Insurance

Exercise 18

The table shows the cost of insuring a motor cycle.

Age of insured in years	Size of engine	Insurance Cover	
		Third Party, Fire and Theft	Comprehensive
16	up to 50 cc	£80	£170
17 to 20	up to 50 cc	£70	£130
	51 to 150 cc	£90	£210
	151 to 300 cc	£130	£260
21 and over	up to 50 cc	£50	£70
	51 to 150 cc	£60	£100
	151 to 300 cc	£80	£170
	301 to 500 cc	£120	£260
'No claim' bonus: one year 10% two years 25% five years or more 60%			

1. David, aged 18, wishes to insure his 175 cc motor cycle.
   (a) How much will it cost him for comprehensive cover?
   (b) How much will it cost him for 'third party, fire and theft' cover?
   (c) How much will it cost him for comprehensive cover if he has a one year no claim bonus?

2. Steve, aged 24, wishes to insure his 250 cc motor cycle.
   (a) How much will it cost him for comprehensive cover?
   (b) How much will it cost him for comprehensive cover if he has a seven years no claim bonus?

3. Jane, aged 19, wishes to insure her 100 cc motor cycle.
   (a) What is her basic premium for 'third party, fire and theft'?
   (b) She does not have a no claims bonus but her premium is reduced by 15% because she lives in the countryside. How much does she pay?

Copy and complete the table below

Name	Age	Size of engine	Cover	No claim bonus	Special discount	Cost
4. Peter	18	250 cc	comp.	2 years		
5. Alan	26	500 cc	3rd party	4 years		
6. Patrick	17	300 cc	3rd party		5%	
7. Mark	20	300 cc	comp.	3 years		
8. Roger	28	500 cc	comp.	8 years		
9. Gary	16	50 cc	3rd party			
10. Paul	23	275 cc	comp.	5 years		
11. John	18	250 cc	3rd party		15%	
12. Jim	22	350 cc	3rd party	2 years		

Pay rises

Exercise 19

1. John works for company A and during 1987 he earns £160 per week. From January 1st 1988 company A offer John an extra 5% on his wages and John accepts this offer and is paid this new wage for 52 weeks in 1988.
   (a) How much is John paid each week in 1988?
   (b) How much does John earn in the whole of 1988?

2. Steve works for company B and during 1987 he also earns £160 per week. From January 1st 1988 company B offer Steve an extra 5% but Steve does not accept this and he goes on strike for six weeks, during which time he receives no pay. After six weeks of the strike, company B offer Steve 10% and he immediately accepts this and receives his increased pay for the rest of 1988.
   (a) How much is Steve paid after the strike?
   (b) How much does Steve earn in the whole of 1988?

3. Ann also earns £160 per week during 1987 and she also goes on strike for the first six weeks of 1988. At the end of her strike she accepts a pay offer of 15% and she receives her increased pay for the rest of 1988.
   (a) How much is Ann paid after the strike?
   (b) How much does Ann earn in the whole of 1988?

4. At the beginning of the year the wages of three people working for the same firm are as follows:
   Cleaner £80 per week;
   Secretary £115 per week;
   Personnel manager £15 080 per year.
   (a) The firm awards all of its employees a pay rise of 5%.
      (i) What is the pay increase for a cleaner?
      (ii) What is the pay increase for a secretary?
      (iii) How much does the personnel manager earn in one week before the pay rise?
      (iv) What is the weekly pay increase for the personnel manager?

   (b) The firm's computer makes a mistake with pay increases and awards an increase of 12% for everyone instead of 5%.
      (i) What is the pay increase for a cleaner?
      (ii) What is the pay increase for a secretary?
      (iii) What is the weekly pay increase for the personnel manager?

5. A shop assistant earns £65 per week. She receives a pay rise of 8%. After stoppages for tax and insurance she actually receives 60% of the increase.
   (a) What is the increase in her pay *before* stoppages?
   (b) How much extra money does she receive in her pay packet after stoppages?

6. A car mechanic earns £180 per week. He receives a pay rise of 7%. After stoppages for tax and insurance he actually receives 60% of the increase.
   (a) What is the increase in his pay *before* stoppages?
   (b) How much extra money does he receive in his pay packet after stoppages?

7. An airline pilot earns £17 940 per year. She receives a pay rise of 5.6%. After stoppages for tax and insurance she actually receives only 55% of the increase.
   (a) How much does she earn per week?
   (b) What is the increase in her weekly pay *before* stoppages?
   (c) How much extra money does she actually receive each week after stoppages? Give the answer to the nearest penny.

8. A judge earns £35 040 per year. Parliament awards him a pay rise of 6.2%. After stoppages for tax and insurance he actually receives only 42% of the increase.
   (a) How much does he earn each month?
   (b) What is the increase in his monthly pay before stoppages?
   (c) How much extra money does he actually receive each month after stoppages? Give the answer to the nearest penny.

Income tax

The tax which an employee pays on his income depends on
(a) how much he is paid
(b) his allowances
(c) the rate of taxation.

Tax is paid only on the 'taxable income'.
(i) Taxable income =
   Total income − allowances.

Allowances depend on whether a person is married or single and on various expenses involved in doing the job.
You can check your allowances by looking at the 'Tax Code Number' on your payslip.

(ii) Allowances =
   (Tax Code Number) × 10

A man earns £6500 per year. If his Tax Code Number is 238, calculate his taxable income.

Allowances = 238 × 10 = £2380.
Taxable income = £6500 − £2380
              = £4120.

Exercise 20

Calculate the taxable income from the details given.

	Earnings	Tax Code Number
1.	£3500 per year	213
2.	£5000 per year	274
3.	£8000 per year	315
4.	£4200 per year	289
5.	£3650 per year	265
6.	£9800 per year	341
7.	£8655 per year	286
8.	£600 per month	412
9.	£450 per month	263
10.	£825 per month	311
11.	£710 per month	278
12.	£985 per month	415
13.	£160 per week	342
14.	£144 per week	214
15.	£180 per week	289

A woman earns £95 per week and her Tax Code Number is 215. Find the total amount of tax paid in a year when the tax rate is 30%.

Amount earned in year = £95 × 52
                      = £4940

Allowances = 215 × 10 = £2150

∴ Taxable income = £4940 − £2150
                 = £2790

Tax paid = 30% of £2790
         = $\frac{30}{100} \times \frac{2790}{1}$ = £837

Exercise 21

In all questions the tax rate is 30%.
1. A man earns £110 per week and his Tax Code Number is 304. Find the total amount of tax paid in a year.
2. A man earns £204 per week and his Tax Code Number is 361. Find the total amount of tax paid in a year.
3. Ann earns £165 per week. How much tax does she pay in a year if her Tax Code Number is 247?
4. John earns £148.50 per week. How much tax does he pay in a year if his Tax Code Number is 302?
5. Louise earns a salary of £620 per month. How much tax does she pay in a year if her Tax Code Number is 342?
6. David earns £950 per month and his Tax Code Number is 357. Find the total amount of tax paid in a year.
7. Mr Tebbit's salary is £9650 per year and his Tax Code Number is 465. Find the total amount of tax paid in a year.

In questions 8 to 15, find the yearly income tax.

	Earnings	Tax Code Number
8.	£4800 per year	310
9.	£850 per month	267
10.	£85 per week	180
11.	£124 per week	253
12.	£4980 per year	384
13.	£1200 per month	462
14.	£235 per week	318
15.	£760 per month	427

1.4 APPROXIMATIONS

(a) 2.486 = 2.5, correct to 2 significant
     ↑   figures.

(b) 31.924 = 31.9 (to 3 s.f.)
        ↑

(c) 45671 = 45700 (to 3 s.f.)
       ↑

(d) 3.2136 = 3.214, correct to 3 decimal
        ↑   places.

(e) 0.455 = 0.46 (to 2 D.P.)
        ↑

(f) 13.246 = 13.2 (to 1 D.P.)
         ↑

In each case look at the figure marked with
an arrow to see if it is '5 or more'.

Exercise 22

In questions **1** to **10** write the numbers correct to
three significant figures.

1. 2.3462	**2.** 0.81438
3. 26.241	**4.** 35.55
5. 112.74	**6.** 210.82
7. 0.8254	**8.** 0.031162
9. 5.6041	**10.** 13.547

In questions **11** to **20** write the numbers correct
to two significant figures.

11. 5.894	**12.** 1.232
13. 0.5456	**14.** 0.7163
15. 0.1443	**16.** 1.831
17. 24.83	**18.** 31.37
19. 8.743	**20.** 35.65

In questions **21** to **30** write the numbers correct
to four significant figures.

21. 486.72	**22.** 500.36
23. 2.8888	**24.** 3.1125
25. 0.071542	**26.** 3.0405
27. 2463.5	**28.** 488 852
29. 642 628	**30.** 111 224

In questions **31** to **60** write the numbers to the
degree of accuracy indicated.

31. 0.5126 (3 s.f.)	**32.** 5.821 (2 s.f.)
33. 65.89 (2 s.f.)	**34.** 587.55 (4 s.f.)
35. 0.581 (1 s.f.)	**36.** 0.0713 (1 s.f.)
37. 5.8354 (3 s.f.)	**38.** 87.84 (2 s.f.)
39. 2482 (2 s.f.)	**40.** 52 666 (3 s.f.)
41. 6.851 (1 s.f.)	**42.** 0.3142 (1 s.f.)
43. 5240 (1 s.f.)	**44.** 34.62 (3 s.f.)
45. 63 840 (3 s.f.)	**46.** 0.0574 (2 s.f.)
47. 0.0333 (1 s.f.)	**48.** 115.62 (3 s.f.)
49. 84 888 (2 s.f.)	**50.** 5.0071 (3 s.f.)
51. 5.0063 (3 s.f.)	**52.** 18.195 (2 s.f.)
53. 3.4961 (3 s.f.)	**54.** 21.982 (3 s.f.)
55. 9.642 (1 s.f.)	**56.** 0.7975 (2 s.f.)
57. 3.982 (2 s.f.)	**58.** 7.981 (2 s.f.)
59. 3.296 (3 s.f.)	**60.** 83.82 (1 s.f.)

Exercise 23

In questions **1** to **10** write the numbers correct to
two decimal places (2 D.P.).

1. 5.381	**2.** 11.0482
3. 0.414	**4.** 0.3666
5. 8.015	**6.** 87.044
7. 9.0062	**8.** 0.0724
9. 0.0685	**10.** 5.1555

In questions **11** to **20** write the numbers correct
to one decimal place.

11. 8.424	**12.** 0.7413
13. 0.382	**14.** 0.095
15. 6.083	**16.** 19.53
17. 8.111	**18.** 7.071
19. 219.63	**20.** 80.89

In questions **21** to **40** write the numbers to the
degree of accuracy indicated.

21. 8.155 (2 D.P.)	**22.** 3.042 (1 D.P.)
23. 0.5454 (3 D.P.)	**24.** 0.005 55 (4 D.P.)
25. 0.7071 (2 D.P.)	**26.** 6.8271 (2 D.P.)
27. 0.8413 (1 D.P.)	**28.** 19.646 (2 D.P.)
29. 0.071 35 (4 D.P.)	**30.** 60.051 (1 D.P.)
31. 0.551 (2 D.P.)	**32.** 0.071 11 (4 D.P.)
33. 8.821 (1 D.P.)	**34.** 6.044 (2 D.P.)
35. 3.0129 (3 D.P.)	**36.** 18.8201 (3 D.P.)
37. 4.005 (2 D.P.)	**38.** 0.0791 (2 D.P.)
39. 8.061 (1 D.P.)	**40.** 12.865 (1 D.P.)

1.5 . STANDARD FORM

Reminder: $66\,000 = 6.6 \times 10^4$
$125\,000 = 1.25 \times 10^5$
$0.000\,76 = 7.6 \times 10^{-4}$
$0.000\,000\,4 = 4.0 \times 10^{-7}$

Exercise 24

Write the following numbers in standard form.

1. 5500
2. 61 400
3. 23 000 000
4. 1 700 000
5. 845 000
6. 27 100
7. 6 000 000 000
8. 8 100 000 000
9. 7 400 000
10. 8 960 000
11. 7140
12. 66 000
13. 8 400 000
14. 746 000
15. 200
16. 4400
17. 75
18. 826 000 000
19. 2 million
20. 30 million

21. 0.000 46
22. 0.000 023
23. 0.0041
24. 0.000 000 075 8
25. 0.0823
26. 0.000 095 8
27. 0.000 006 15
28. 0.000 001 52
29. 0.0756
30. 0.006 164
31. 0.000 008 8
32. 0.008 14
33. 0.000 000 009 5
34. 0.074
35. 0.08
36. 0.95
37. 0.000 714
38. 0.999
39. 0.084 15
40. 0.000 045

Exercise 25

Write the following numbers in the usual way.

1. 2.3×10^2
2. 3.4×10^5
3. 4.1×10^3
4. 2.71×10^2
5. 8.2×10^4
6. 3×10^8
7. 9×10^2
8. 2.2×10^5
9. 6.35×10^1
10. 8.95×10^4
11. 4×10^5
12. 1.234×10^3
13. 5.14×10^2
14. 8×10^1
15. 7×10^3
16. 6.05×10^2
17. 8.012×10^4
18. 6×10^7
19. 9.6×10^2
20. 4.2×10^4

21. 4.2×10^{-2}
22. 4.7×10^{-3}
23. 1.6×10^{-3}
24. 8.9×10^{-4}
25. 8.4×10^{-1}
26. 6×10^{-2}
27. 9.51×10^{-4}
28. 2×10^{-5}
29. 8×10^{-5}
30. 4.1×10^{-1}
31. 6.3×10^{-3}
32. 8.04×10^{-3}
33. 5×10^{-2}
34. 6.9×10^{-2}
35. 4.8×10^{-4}
36. 8.95×10^{-1}
37. 6.11×10^{-2}
38. 8×10^{-7}
39. 9×10^{-6}
40. 1.11×10^{-3}

41. 5.2×10^3
42. 9.4×10^{-3}
43. 8×10^{-2}
44. 3.8×10^5
45. 6.7×10^{-4}
46. 6.66×10^{-2}
47. 1.1×10^4
48. 8.1×10^{-3}
49. 7×10^{-1}
50. 5×10^6

Part 2

2.1 THE METRIC SYSTEM

(a) $3.24 \times 100 = 324$
    (Move point two places to the right)

(b) $0.0417 \times 1000 = 41.7$
    (Move point three places to the right)

(c) $63.1 \div 100 = 0.631$
    (Move point two places to the left)

Exercise 1

This exercise provides revision of multiplying and dividing by 10's, 100's, 1000's etc. Do not use a calculator.

1. 0.36×10
2. 0.085×100
3. 0.47×100
4. 0.96×10
5. 5.6×10
6. 0.74×1000
7. 2.3×1000
8. 11.52×100
9. 0.8×100
10. $6.54 \times 10\ 000$
11. $0.075 \div 10$
12. $81.5 \div 1000$
13. $0.047 \div 1000$
14. $6.2 \div 10$
15. $0.52 \div 100$
16. $310 \div 1000$
17. $1.63 \div 10$
18. $7 \div 100$
19. $0.72 \div 100$
20. $4500 \div 100\ 000$
21. $0.047 \times 10\ 000$
22. 6.22×100
23. $82.6 \div 10$
24. $858 \div 10\ 000$
25. 0.007×10
26. $0.073 \div 10$
27. $573 \div 1000$
28. 1.45×1000
29. $264 \div 10\ 000$
30. $6 \times 10\ 000$
31. 0.06×100
32. $0.06 \div 10\ 000$
33. 0.0004×1 million
34. $1.5 \div 100$
35. $85 \div 10$
36. 800×10
37. 6.3×1 million
38. $6000 \div 1$ million
39. $849 \div 1000$
40. $0.000\ 06 \times 10$ million

Metric units

```
Length: 10 mm = 1 cm
        100 cm = 1 m
        1000 m = 1 km
Mass: 1000 g = 1 kg
      1000 kg = 1 t
      (t for tonne)
Volume: 1000 ml = 1 l
        1000 l = 1 m³
        (l for litre)
        Also 1 ml = 1 cm³
```

Exercise 2

Copy and complete.
1. 85 cm =   m
2. 2.4 km =   m
3. 0.63 m =   cm
4. 25 cm =   m
5. 7 mm =   cm
6. 2 cm =   mm
7. 1.2 km =   m
8. 7 m =   cm
9. 0.58 km =   m
10. 815 mm =   m

11. 650 m =   km
12. 25 mm =   cm
13. 5 kg =   g
14. 4.2 kg =   g
15. 6.4 kg =   g
16. 3 kg =   g
17. 0.8 kg =   g
18. 400 g =   kg
19. 2 t =   kg
20. 250 g =   kg

21. 0.5 t =   kg
22. 0.62 t =   kg
23. 7 kg =   t
24. 1500 g =   kg
25. 800 ml =   l
26. 2 l =   ml
27. 1000 ml =   l
28. 4.5 l =   ml
29. 6 l = ml
30. 3 l =   cm³

31. 2 m³ =   l
32. 5.5 m³ =   l
33. 0.9 l =   cm³
34. 600 cm³ =   l
35. 15 m³ =   l
36. 240 ml =   l
37. 28 cm =   m
38. 5.5 m =   cm
39. 305 g =   kg
40. 0.046 km =   m

41. 16 ml =   l
42. 208 mm =   m
43. 28 mm =   cm
44. 27 cm =   m
45. 788 m =   km
46. 14 t =   kg
47. 1.3 kg =   g
48. 90 l =   m³
49. 2.9 t =   kg
50. 19 ml =   l

2.2   IMPERIAL UNITS

Exercise 3

```
(a)     12 inches = 1 foot
        3 feet = 1 yard
        1760 yards = 1 mile
(b)     16 ounces = 1 pound
        14 pounds = 1 stone
        2240 pounds = 1 ton
(c)     8 pints = 1 gallon
```

1. How many inches are there in two feet?
2. How many ounces are there in three pounds?
3. How many feet are there in ten yards?
4. How many pounds are there in two tons?
5. How many pints are there in six gallons?
6. How many yards are there in ten miles?
7. How many inches are there in one yard?
8. How many pounds are there in five stones?
9. How many pints are there in half a gallon?
10. How many yards are there in half a mile?

In questions 11 to 30 copy each statement and fill in the missing numbers.

11. 9 feet =   yards
12. 16 pints =   gallons
13. 2 miles =   yards
14. 5 pounds =   ounces
15. 10 stones =   pounds
16. 4 yards =   feet
17. 4 feet =   inches
18. 10 tons =   pounds
19. 1 mile =   feet
20. 6 feet =   yards

21. 2 feet 6 inches =   inches.
22. 5 feet 2 inches =   inches.
23. 5 stones 6 pounds =   pounds.
24. 7 stones 3 pounds =   pounds.
25. $1\frac{1}{2}$ feet =   inches.
26. $\frac{1}{2}$ pound =   ounces.
27. 4 feet 10 inches =   inches.
28. 6 stones 8 pounds =   pounds.
29. $\frac{1}{4}$ pound =   ounces.
30. 10 stones 12 pounds =   pounds.

Exercise 4

The following conversions are approximate.

1 inch = 2.54 cm   1 pint = 0.568 litre
1 mile = 1.61 km   1 gallon = 4.55 litres
1 km = 0.621 mile   1 litre = 0.22 gallon
                        1 lb = 0.454 kg
                        1 kg = 2.2 lb

In questions **1** to **20** copy each statement and fill in the missing numbers.

1. 10 inches =   cm
2. 10 miles =   km
3. 2 kg =   lb
4. 2 km =   miles
5. 10 gallons =   litres
6. 10 litres =   gallons
7. 5 kg =   lb
8. 100 km =   miles
9. 6 inches =   cm
10. 4 miles =   km

11. 8 gallons =   litres
12. 4 pints =   litres
13. 25 kg =   lb
14. 1000 miles =   km
15. 12 km =   miles
16. 10 lb =   kg
17. 3 inches =   cm
18. 20 litres =   gallons
19. 6 litres =   gallons
20. 7 km =   miles

2.3   PROBLEMS

The next exercises provide practice in using basic arithmetic to solve problems in a wide variety of situations.

Exercise 5

1. 35 000 people saw Spurs play one Saturday. Calculate the takings at the gate if 25 000 stood for £2 each and 10 000 were seated at £3.50 each.

2. A school party caught a train at Victoria station at 0850 and arrived at Dover at 1055. The return train left Dover at 1923 and took exactly the same time on the journey as the morning train. Calculate the time at which the return train arrived at Victoria.

3. A car uses 13 litres of fuel for every 100 km travelled. Calculate the cost, in £, of travelling 300 km if petrol costs 45p per litre.

4. If £1 is equivalent to $1.45,
   (a) how many dollars are equivalent to £50,
   (b) how many dollars are equivalent to 60p?

5. A worker is paid a basic weekly wage of £20 plus 25p for each item completed. How many items must be completed in a week when he earns a total of £95.50?

6. On the 1st January 1986 Mr Jones has £2754.26 in a bank account. During the year he withdraws £800 and is credited with interest of £65.84 and £43.48. How much is in his account on 1st January 1987?

7. The contents of a house have a total value of £8800. Calculate the insurance premium when the rate is 16p per £100 insured.

8. Write down the next two numbers in each of the following sequences.
   (a) 4, 9, 14, 19, . . .
   (b) 68, 56, 44, . . .
   (c) 5, 6, 4, 7, 3, . . .
   (d) 162, 54, 18, 6, . . .

9. A shopkeeper buys tea at £1.15 per kg and sells it at 32p per 100 g. How much profit does he make per kg?

10. A television programme starts at 1755 and ends at 2050. How many hours and minutes does the programme last?

Exercise 6

1. A private hospital charges its patients £150 per day. How much will it cost to stay in this hospital for six days?

2. Mrs Brown earned £76 plus a bonus of £26 in one week. Income tax of £18 was deducted from her wages. Work out her take-home pay.

3. One Saturday last season only 32,163 people watched all the matches in the Scottish League division two. This was 17,584 fewer than the number watching the Manchester United–QPR game. How many people watched the game between Manchester United and QPR?

4. How many shirts costing £15 could you buy for £100?

5. A factory produces 1550 televisions every day. The workers go on strike for nine days. How many televisions are lost because of the strike?

6. A coach journey is going to cost £200. This cost is to be shared by 16 people. How much will each person have to pay?

7. Mr Simpson wants to buy a car costing £4755. The garage offers him a trade-in of £1240 for his old car. How much extra cash does he need to buy the car?

8. An office building has twelve floors and each floor has twenty windows. A window cleaner charges 50p per window. How much will he charge to clean all the windows in the building?

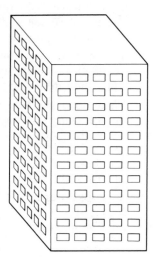

9. An old sailor keeps all of his savings in gold. Altogether the gold weighs ten pounds. One day the price of gold goes up by $40 an ounce to $520 an ounce.
(a) By how much did his gold rise in value?
(b) How much was it worth after the rise? (1 pound = 16 ounces).

10. This packet of sugar cubes costs 60p

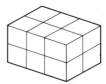

How much would you have to pay for this packet?

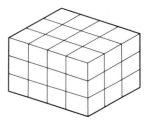

Exercise 7

1. A 7-day holiday in Germany costs £302. Find the average cost per day, correct to the nearest pound.

2. There are 1150 pupils in a school. If 52% of the pupils are girls, how many boys are there?

3. John Lowe made darts history in 1984 with the first ever perfect game played in a tournament, 501 scored in just nine darts. He won a special prize of £100 000 from the sponsors of the tournament. His first eight darts were six treble 20s, treble 17 and treble 18.
(a) What did he score with the ninth dart?
(b) How much did he win per dart thrown, to the nearest pound?

4. Eight cans of beer cost £1.28. How many cans of beer could be bought for £8?

5. Reduce the cost of each of the following items by one quarter of its price:
(a) Video recorder: £480
(b) Washing machine: £300
(c) Record: £5.

6. 5, 9, 11, 21, 33, 38, 39
Which of the above numbers are:
(a) divisible by 3   (b) prime numbers
(c) even numbers   (d) divisible by 7?

7. Write the following to the degree of accuracy stated:
(a) 7.243 (to 1 D.P.)   (b) 11.275 (to 2 D.P.)
(c) 0.115 (to 1 D.P.)   (d) 0.0255 (to 3 D.P.)
(e) 28.21 (to 1 D.P.)   (f) 0.0072 (to 2 D.P.)

8. Work out, without using a calculator.
(a) 0.6 + 2.72   (b) 3.21 − 1.6
(c) 2.8 − 1.34   (d) 8 − 3.6
(e) 100 × 0.062   (f) 27.4 ÷ 10

9. A rectangular wheat field is 200 m by 400 m. One hectare is 10 000 m^2 and each hectare produces 3 tonnes of wheat.
(a) What is the area of the field in hectares?
(b) How much wheat is produced in this field?

10. A powerful computer is hired out at a rate of 50p per minute. How much will it cost to hire the computer from 06 30 to 18 00?

Exercise 8

1. A bookseller bought 400 copies of a book. He sold: 108 in week 1
145 in week 2
74 in week 3.
How many books did he have left after week 3?

2. A market trader sells a coat at a profit of 80% on the cost price of £35. For how much does he sell the coat?

3. A man's heart beats on average 68 times every minute.
(a) How many times will his heart beat in 10 minutes?
(b) How many times will his heart beat between 1800 and 2120?

4. How many 50 ml bottles can be filled from a jar containing 7 litres of liquid?

7 litres

50 ml

5. What fraction of £1 is
(a) 10p   (b) 5p   (c) 50p   (d) 75p?

6. Write as a single number:
(a) 7^2 (b) 1^3 (c) 9^2
(d) 2^2 + 3^2 (e) 10^2 + 5^2 (f) 8^2 − 6^2

7. Karen is 16 years old and her father is 25 years older than her. Karen's mother is 4 years younger than her father. How old is Karen's mother?

8. A coach holds 60 people. How many people are in the coach when it is
(a) half full?
(b) three-quarters full?
(c) four-fifths full?

9. Find the figures A, B and C if

$$\begin{array}{r} 32A \\ 6B3 \\ + \; C27 \\ \hline 1764 \end{array}$$

10. The numbers '5' and '4' multiply to give 20 and add up to 9. Find two numbers which:
(a) multiply to give 30 and add up to 11.
(b) multiply to give 36 and add up to 15.
(c) multiply to give 36 and add up to 13.

Exercise 9

1. Four dozen bags of grain weigh 2016 kg. How much does each bag weigh?

2. A swimming pool 20 m by 12 m contains water to a uniform depth of $1\frac{1}{2}$ m. 1 m^3 of water weighs 1000 kg. What is the weight of the water in the pool?

3. A wall measuring 3 m by 2 m is to be covered with square tiles of side 10 cm.
(a) How many tiles are needed?
(b) If the tiles cost £3.40 for ten, how much will it cost?

4. £60 is shared among three people in the ratio 3:4:5. How much is the smallest share?

5. Change the following 12-hour clock times to 24-hour clock times
(a) 7.30 a.m.
(b) 7.30 p.m.
(c) 1.00 p.m.

6. How many apples costing 8p each can be bought with £1?

7. How many cubes, each of edge 1 cm, are required to fill a box with internal dimensions 5 cm by 8 cm by 3 cm?

8. When a car journey starts, the mileometer reads 42 714 miles. After two hours the mileometer reads 42 858 miles. What is the average speed of the car?

9. The map below, which is not drawn to scale, shows the roads joining towns A, B, C, D, E and F. There are signposts at C and F, giving distances in miles.

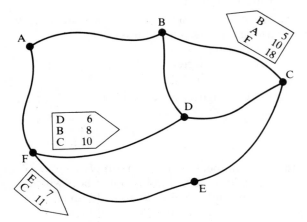

(a) Make a copy of the map and mark on it the lengths of all of the roads.
(b) Work out the *shortest* distance between the following pairs of towns:
   (i)   F and E
   (ii) F and C
   (iii) F and B
   (iv) D and A
   (v)   E and A
   (vi) B and E

10. I think of a number. If I add 5 and then divide the result by 2 the answer is 8. What number was I thinking of?

Exercise 10

1. A packet of baby food makes 100 feeds. A baby has 5 feeds a day. How many days will the packet last?

2. John is 12 years old and his father is 28 years older than he is. John's mother is 3 years younger than his father. How old is John's mother?

3. Which is greater and by how much: (10% of £600) or (25% of £210)?

4. A rectangular box, without a lid, is to be made from cardboard.

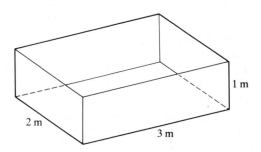

(a) What area of cardboard is required?
(b) What is the volume of the box?

5. (a) Which four coins make a total of 77p?
   (b) Which five coins make a total of 86p?
   (c) Which five coins make a total of £1.57?

6. Arrange the following numbers in order, smallest first:
8711, 8171, 8117, 817, 8710

7. How much change would I get from £100 after buying two records at £4.95 each, three books at £1.95 each and a turkey for £6.34?

8. A large wheel in a factory turns once every 15 s. How many rotations will it make in 2 hours?

9. Nine bars of chocolate weigh 468 g. They cost £3.15 altogether.
   (a) How much does one bar weigh?
   (b) How much does one bar cost?
   (c) How many bars can I buy for £5.25?

10. The numbers '6' and '2' have a sum of 8 and a product of 12. Find two numbers:
   (a) with a sum of 7 and a product of 12,
   (b) with a sum of 7 and a product of 10,
   (c) with a sum of 11 and a product of 28.

Exercise 11

1. How many stamps each costing 16p can be bought for £1?

2. A typist is paid £4.15 per hour. How much does she earn in a week when she works 40 hours?

3. It needs 100 g of flour to make 20 small cakes. How much flour is needed to make 30 of these cakes?

4. One litre of petrol costs 41.2p and one litre of oil costs 82p.
  (a) Find the cost of 100 litres of petrol
  (b) Find the cost of 10 litres of oil
  (c) Find the total cost of 40 litres of petrol and 20 litres of oil
  (d) Find the total cost of 50 litres of petrol and 8 litres of oil.

5. Calculate the area of the shape below.

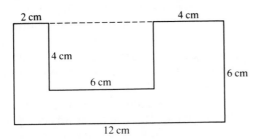

6. A model train is built to a scale of 1:50. The height of the engine of the actual train is 250 cm. Find the height of the engine of the model.

7. Steven has caught ten more fish than Peter and they have caught fifty altogether between them. How many fish has each caught?

8. How many minutes are there between:
  (a) 09 20 and 11 10,
  (b) 07 15 and 10 00,
  (c) 14 45 and 17 15,
  (d) 02 10 and 06 10?

9. Two numbers m and z are such that z is greater than 10 and m is less than 8. Arrange the numbers 9, z and m in order of size, starting with the smallest.

10. Draw the next member of the sequence

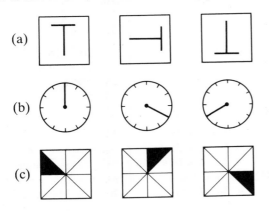

Exercise 12

1. A greengrocer sells 9 kg of potatoes for £2.79.
  Find: (a) the cost of 1 kg,
         (b) how many kg can be bought for £1.86.

2. Arrange the following numbers in order, smallest first:
  2061, 2601, 2106, 2616, 2016.

3. It costs 10p per minute to operate a machine. How much will it cost to operate the machine from 11 50 to 13 15?

4. A garden 9 m by 12 m is to be treated with fertilizer. One cup of fertilizer covers an area of 2 m² and one bag of fertilizer is sufficient for 18 cups.
  (a) Find the area of the garden.
  (b) Find the number of bags of fertilizer needed.

5. Copy and complete the pattern below.

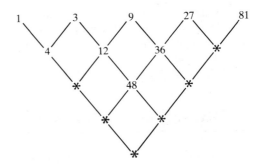

6. A man is 35 cm taller than his daughter, who is 5 cm shorter than her mother. The man was born in 1949 and is 1.80 m tall. How tall is the wife?

7. A car travels from 10 25 to 10 55 at a speed of 84 km/h. How far does it go?

8. During a sale all prices are reduced by 10%. What is the sale price of an article with a marked price of
  (a) £15   (b) £24   (c) £12.50?

9. An examination is marked out of a total of 120 marks. How many marks did Alan get if he scored 65% of the marks?

10. A man gives £3.00 to his two children so that his daughter receives 40p more than his son. How much does the daughter receive?

Exercise 13

1. A man starts work each day at 08 00 and works until 17 30. He stops working for one hour at lunchtime. How many hours does he work in a 5-day week?

2. Place the following numbers in order of size, smallest first:
0.14, 0.05, 0.062, 0.41, 0.009.

3. The diagram below shows the map of a farm which grows four different crops in the regions shown.

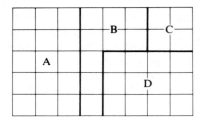

Each square represents one acre.
(a) What is the total area of the farm?
(b) What area is used for crop A?
(c) What percentage of the farm is used for
   (i) crop C   (ii) crop D
   (iii) crop A   (iv) crop B?

4. One afternoon there are four soccer matches and three rugby matches all being played at the same time. Each soccer team has 11 players and each rugby team has 15 players. How many players are in action altogether?

5. A steel bar of length 2 m is cut into two pieces so that one piece is 8 cm longer than the other. How long is the longer piece?

6. The petrol tank of a car will hold 60 litres, but it contains only 54 litres. To fill it up a bottle full of petrol must be poured in 5 times. Find the capacity of the bottle.

7. A boat journey starts at 08 15. It travels 80.5 km at a speed of 23 km/h. When does the journey finish?

8. An adult and 5 children were charged a total entrance fee of £8. The adult was charged £2 and the children were all charged the same amount. How much was each child charged?

9. A man sells a car at a loss of 30% on the original cost price of £3800. How much does he receive for the car?

10. Write as a single number:
   (a) 4^2 (b) 6^2 (c) 3^3
   (d) 10^4 (e) 3×5^2 (f) 4×10^2

2.4 ORDER OF OPERATIONS

Always perform operations in the following order:
   (a) Brackets
   (b) Divide and multiply
   (c) Add and subtract.

Work out (a) $7 + 6 \div 3$
         (b) $8 - 4 \times 2$
         (c) $6 \times 4 - 8 \div 2$

(a) $7 + 6 \div 3 = 7 + 2 = 9$
(b) $8 - 4 \times 2 = 8 - 8 = 0$
(c) $6 \times 4 - 8 \div 2 = 24 - 4 = 20$

Exercise 14

Work out
1. $9 + 2 \times 2$
2. $6 + 8 \div 2$
3. $12 - 8 \div 1$
4. $3 \times 5 - 7$
5. $16 \div 4 - 2$
6. $11 - 3 \times 3$
7. $4 + 7 \times 3$
8. $4 \times 5 - 3$
9. $8 + 12 \div 6$
10. $3 + 7 \times 4$
11. $17 - 9 \div 9$
12. $23 + 10 \div 5$
13. $30 + 16 \div 8$
14. $5 \times 6 - 14$
15. $6 \times 3 + 4$
16. $12 \div 2 + 8$
17. $15 - 8 \div 1$
18. $9 - 2 \times 4$
19. $5 + 4 \div 8$
20. $6 \times 7 + 4$
21. $15 \div 3 + 25$
22. $26 - 18 \div 3$
23. $16 \times 2 - 20$
24. $14 + 16 \div 8$
25. $8 - 0 \div 3$
26. $9 \times 8 - 61$
27. $11 - 3 \div 3$
28. $51 - 6 \times 7$
29. $8 \div 1 - 6$
30. $633 \div 3 + 10$
31. $3 \times 2 + 4 \times 1$
32. $4 \times 8 + 2 \times 3$
33. $2 \times 5 + 3 \times 3$
34. $6 \times 6 - 5 \times 5$
35. $7 \times 2 - 4 \times 0$
36. $7 \times 3 - 0 \times 8$
37. $24 \div 6 + 7 \times 2$
38. $6 \div 6 + 7 \times 7$
39. $8 \times 3 - 9 \div 3$
40. $8 \times 3 - 50 \div 5$

41. $16 \div 8 + 8 \times 4$

43. $6 \times 2 - 18 \div 9$

45. $27 \div 3 - 14 \div 2$

47. $3 \times 5 + 8 \times 3$

49. $36 \div 9 - 8 \div 8$

42. $10 \div 10 + 13 \times 5$

44. $0.1 \div 0.1 + 4 \times 5$

46. $28 \div 7 - 15 \div 5$

48. $9 \times 2 + 36 \div 6$

50. $54 \div 9 - 2 \times 2$

51. $9 - 3 \times 2 + 1$

53. $10 + 4 \times 3 - 8$

55. $7 - 8 \div 2 - 1$

57. $4 + 6 \times 1 - 10$

59. $3 + 12 \div 2 + 3$

61. $6 \times 3 + 4 \div 4$

63. $8 \times 2 - 2 \times 5$

65. $10 \div 2 - 3 \div 1$

67. $6 + 4 \times 4 - 7$

69. $7 + 16 \div 8 - 9$

71. $18 \div 2 + 8 \times 8$

73. $8 + 200 \div 4 - 41$

75. $500 - 7 \times 70 + 3$

77. $55 - 600 \div 12 + 5$

79. $6 \times 5 - 72 \div 8$

52. $7 - 20 \div 5 + 6$

54. $8 + 6 \times 6 - 40$

56. $30 \div 2 - 3 \times 4$

58. $22 - 3 \times 7 - 1$

60. $11 + 8 \div 2 - 5$

62. $42 \div 7 - 8 \times 0$

64. $3 + 5 \times 5 - 20$

66. $7 \times 7 + 2 \times 2$

68. $607 \times 1 - 7 \div 3.5$

70. $30 - 6 \times 4 + 3$

72. $13 - 84 \div 7 + 7$

74. $600 \div 10 - 8 \times 7$

76. $8 + 1.7 \times 0 - 7$

78. $6 + 2 \div 0.5 + 1$

80. $8 - 20 \times 0.1 - 2$

27. $7 + (50 - 43) \times 7$

29. $48 \div (19 - 7) + 5$

31. $60 - (2 \div 2) \times 10$

33. $10 + 7 \times (9 - 7)$

35. $(11 - 8) \times 7 + 11$

37. $5 \times (4 + 5) - 15$

39. $3 + 3 \times (8 - 2)$

28. $45 \div (20 - 11) - 2$

30. $(31 - 21) \times 10 - 65$

32. $17 + 4 \times (20 - 20)$

34. $8 + (11 - 4) \times 2$

36. $34 - 10 \times (9 - 7)$

38. $18 - 2 \times (24 \div 12)$

40. $7 - (13 + 11) \div 4$

41. $(6 - 3) \times 4 - (10 + 4) \div 7$

42. $(12 - 7) \times 2 - (6 + 5) \times 0$

43. $3 \times (8 - 5) + (15 - 9) \div 8$

44. $(8 \div 4) \times 3 + (9 - 8) \times 2$

45. $(38 - 6 \times 6) + (12 + 4 \times 2)$

46. $(17 - 5 \times 3) - (8 - 8 \div 1)$

47. $(5 \times 4 - 15) + (3 + 5 \times 3)$

48. $(7 + 2 \times 2) - (9 - 3 \times 2)$

49. $(9 + 7) \div 4 + 3 \times (11 - 8)$

50. $16 - 2 \times (8 \div 1) + (8 + 4) \div 6$

51. $(20 - 5 \times 3) \times 2 - 4 \div 4$

52. $(8 + 3 \times 1) \div 11 - (3 - 2 \times 1)$

53. $12 - (7 + 9) \div 4 + 3$

54. $28 - [(3 + 7) \div 2] \times 2$

55. $16 + 2 \times [(3 - 2) \times 2 + 1]$

56. $8 + [2 + 3 \times (8 - 5)]$

57. $[(10 - 7) \times 3] \times 3 - 7$

58. $(50 - 9 \times 5) \times 2 + 40 \div 8$

59. $[(2 - 2) \times 11 + 4] \times 3$

60. $[(14 - (8 - 6) \times 2)] \times 4 - 1$

61. $\dfrac{(15 + 24)}{(9 - 6)}$

62. $\dfrac{(36 - 11)}{(14 - 9)}$

63. $\dfrac{(30 - 3 \times 2)}{(4 + 2 \times 1)}$

64. $\dfrac{(12 + 4 \times 2)}{(15 - 7 \times 2)}$

65. $\dfrac{(6 + 9 \times 8)}{(5 - 8 \div 4)}$

66. $\dfrac{(62 - 4 \times 3)}{(4 + 3 \times 2)}$

Work out (a) $5 + (28 + 5) \div 3$

(b) $7 + (9 - 5) \times 4 - (9 + 5) \div 7$

(a) $5 + (28 + 5) \div 3 = 5 + 33 \div 3$
$= 5 + 11$
$= 16$

(b) $\quad 7 + (9 - 5) \times 4 - (9 + 5) \div 7$
$= 7 + 4 \times 4 - 14 \div 7$
$= 7 + 16 - 2$
$= 21$

Exercise 15

Work out

1. $7 + (9 - 5) \times 3$

3. $8 + (8 + 3) \times 2$

5. $(12 + 2) \div 2 - 5$

7. $4 + 2 \times (10 - 5)$

9. $20 - (11 - 7) \times 4$

2. $16 - (6 + 1) \times 2$

4. $(18 - 7) \times 3 + 10$

6. $8 - 12 \div (9 - 6)$

8. $(12 \div 3) \times 5 - 19$

10. $14 - (3 + 4) \times 2$

11. $12 + (17 - 13) \times 5$

13. $7 \times (26 - 21) - 14$

15. $20 \div (7 - 3) + 26$

17. $6 + 7 \times (10 - 3)$

19. $45 - 9 \times (11 - 6)$

21. $(3 + 4) \times 6 - 10$

23. $14 - (27 - 12) \div 5$

25. $(36 + 14) \div 10 + 16$

12. $5 + (7 + 3) \times 3$

14. $5 \times (5 + 2) - 15$

16. $19 - (18 + 6) \div 3$

18. $26 + (17 + 7) \div 12$

20. $(33 - 29) \times 7 + 5$

22. $80 - (8 + 5) \div 13$

24. $9 + 40 \div (12 - 4)$

26. $20 + 7 \times (15 - 9)$

Exercise 16

This exercise is more difficult. Write down each question and find the missing signs. $(+, -, \times, \div)$. There are no brackets.

1. 7   5   4 = 27
2. 3   5   10 = 25
3. 4   2   3 = 5
4. 11   3   3 = 20
5. 31   10   2 = 11
6. 10   6   5 = 40
7. 4   8   7 = 25
8. 12   9   2 = 30
9. 18   4   4 = 2
10. 28   10   2 = 8
11. 21   3   5 = 2
12. 7   3   3 = 16
13. 10   2   3 = 8
14. 10   3   12 = 42
15. 18   3   7 = 13
16. 31   40   5 = 39
17. 15   16   4 = 11
18. 15   8   9 = 87
19. 37   35   5 = 44
20. 11   5   9 = 64
21. 8   3   2   4 = 10
22. 12   3   3   1 = 4
23. 11   4   1   6 = 9
24. 15   5   2   4 = 11
25. 7   2   3   3 = 5
26. 12   2   3   4 = 22
27. 8   9   6   11 = 6
28. 20   20   9   0 = 1
29. 20   30   10   8 = 25
30. 30   6   11   11 = 85

2.5   PERCENTAGE INCREASE AND DECREASE

Percentage increase =
$\dfrac{\text{(actual increase)}}{\text{(original value)}} \times \dfrac{100}{1}$

The price of a car is increased from £6400 to £6800

Percentage increase $= \dfrac{400}{6400} \times \dfrac{100}{1}$

$= 6\frac{1}{4}\%$

	Original price	Final price
11.	$2.50	$3.00
12.	$18	$24
13.	$400	$450
14.	£3.20	£3.52
15.	£5.80	£6.09

In questions **16** to **25** calculate the percentage decrease.

	Original price	Final price
16.	£800	£600
17.	£50	£40
18.	£120	£105
19.	£420	£280
20.	£6000	£1200
21.	$880	$836
22.	$15 000	$14 100
23.	$7.50	$6.00
24.	£8.20	£7.79
25.	£16 000	£15 600

Exercise 17

In questions **1** to **15** calculate the percentage increase.

	Original price	Final price
1.	£50	£54
2.	£80	£88
3.	£180	£225
4.	£100	£102
5.	£75	£78
6.	£400	£410
7.	£5000	£6000
8.	£210	£315
9.	£600	£690
10.	$4000	$7200

Exercise 18

Find the percentage profit/loss using the formula:

$$\text{percentage profit} = \frac{\text{(actual profit)}}{\text{(cost price)}} \times \frac{100}{1}$$

Give the answers correct to one decimal place.

	Cost price	Selling price
1.	£11	£15
2.	£21	£25
3.	£36	£43
4.	£41	£50
5.	£411	£461
6.	£5.32	£5.82
7.	£6.14	£7.00
8.	£2.13	£2.50
9.	£6.11	£8.11
10.	£18.15	£20
11.	£20	£18.47
12.	£17	£11
13.	£13	£9
14.	£211	£200
15.	£8.15	£7
16.	£2.62	£3
17.	£1.52	£1.81
18.	$13.50	$13.98
19.	$3.05	$4.00
20.	$1705	$1816

Exercise 19

1. The number of people employed by a firm increased from 250 to 280. Calculate the percentage increase in the workforce.

2. During the first four weeks of her life a baby's weight increases from 3000 g to 3870 g. Calculate the percentage increase in the baby's weight.

3. Before cooking, a joint of meat weighs 2.5 kg. After cooking the same joint of meat weighs only 2.1 kg. Calculate the percentage decrease in the weight of the joint.

4. When cold, an iron rod is 200 cm long. After being heated, the length increases to 200.5 cm. Calculate the percentage increase in the length of the rod.

5. A man buys a car for £4000 and sells it for £4600. Calculate the percentage profit.

6. A shopkeeper buys jumpers for £6.20 and sells them for £9.99. Calculate the percentage profit correct to one decimal place.

7. A grocer buys bananas at 20p per pound but after the fruit are spoiled he has to sell them at only 17p per pound. Calculate the percentage loss.

8. Before a service the petrol consumption of a car was 31 miles per gallon. After the service the consumption improved to 35.4 miles per gallon. Calculate the percentage improvement in the petrol consumption, correct to one decimal place.

31 m.p.g.   35.4 m.p.g.

9. After an outbreak of smallpox, the population of a town went down from 22 315 to 21 987. Calculate the percentage reduction, correct to one decimal place.

10. In 1986 a tennis player earned £2 410 200. In 1987 the same player earned £2 985 010. Calculate the percentage increase in his income, correct to one decimal place.

Exercise 20

This exercise is more difficult.

1. A shopkeeper bought 40 articles for £10 and sold them at 32p each. Calculate
   (a) the cost price of each article.
   (b) the total selling price of the 40 articles.
   (c) the total profit.
   (d) the percentage profit.

2. A grocer bought a crate of 50 tins of peaches at 20p per tin.
   (a) Find the total cost of the crate of peaches.
   (b) He sold all the tins at 27p per tin.
      (i) How much profit did he make?
      (ii) Express this profit as a percentage of his total cost price.

3. A shopkeeper bought a crate of 40 tins of pears at 25p per tin.
(a) Find the total cost of the crate of pears.
(b) He sold 10 tins at 37p per tin, and the rest of the crate at 35p per tin.
  (i) How much profit did he make?
  (ii) Express this profit as a percentage of his total cost price.

4. (a) A shopkeeper buys a number of chairs for £12 each and marks them for sale at £15 each. What percentage profit does he make on the cost price if he sells one chair?
(b) To encourage business he offers 10% off all orders for 6 or more chairs
  (i) How much does he receive for an order of 10 chairs?
  (ii) What percentage profit does he make on the cost price when he allows the discount?

5. ABCD is a square of side 100 cm. Side AB is increased by 20% and side AD is reduced by 25% to form rectangle APQR.

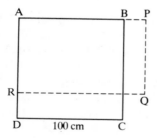

(a) Calculate (i) the length of AP
          (ii) the length of AR
          (iii) the area of square ABCD
          (iv) the area of rectangle APQR.
(b) By what percentage has the area of the square been reduced?

6. ABCD is a square of side 50 cm. Side AB is increased by 16% and side AD is reduced by 40% to form rectangle AKLM.

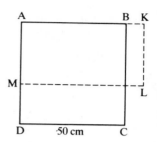

(a) Calculate (i) the length of AK
          (ii) the length of AM.
          (iii) the area of square ABCD
          (iv) the area of rectangle AKLM
(b) By what percentage has the area of the square ABCD been reduced?

7. A jacket costs £60 to make and the shopkeeper adds 25% to give the 'marked price'. During a sale all goods in the shop are labelled 'Sale price 10% off marked price'.
(a) What was the marked price before the sale?
(b) How much did a customer pay for the suit during the sale?
(c) What percentage profit did the shopkeeper make on a suit which was sold in the sale?

8. When a house was built in 1986 the total cost was made up of the following:
    wages   £30 000
    materials   £16 000
    overheads   £4 000
(a) Find the total cost of the house in 1986.
(b) In 1987 the cost of wages increased by 10%, the cost of materials increased by 5% and the overheads remained at their previous cost.
  (i) Find the total cost of the house in 1987.
  (ii) Calculate the percentage increase in 1986 to 1987.

2.6 TIMETABLES

BBC 2

9.0	**PAGES FROM CEEFAX.**
10.20	**OPEN UNIVERSITY.**
11.25	**PAGES FROM CEEFAX.**
11.50	**CHAMPION THE WONDER HORSE*:** Lost River (rpt.). A drought brings danger.
12.15	**WINDMILL:** Archive film on animals.
1.10	**STATES OF MIND:** Jonathan Miller talks to Professor Richard Gregory (rpt.).
2.0	**RUGBY SPECIAL:** Highlights of a County Championship match and a Welsh Cup match.
2.30	**TENNIS:** Benson and Hedges Final.
4.15	**UNDER SAIL:** New series.
4.35	**RACHMANINOV MASTERCLASS.**
5.20	**THINKING ALOUD:** Denis Healey joins a discussion on espionage.
6.0	**NEWS REVIEW**, with Moira Stewart.
6.30	**THE MONEY PROGRAMME:** Guns for Sale. A look at Britain's defence industry.
7.15	**THE NATURAL WORLD:** City of Coral. A voyage beneath the Caribbean.
8.5	**COMRADES:** Educating Rita. The first of 12 films about life in the Soviet Union profiles a young trainee teacher.
8.50	**100 GREAT SPORTING MOMENTS:** Daley Thompson's Gold in the Moscow Olympics.
9.10	**FAWLTY TOWERS:** Basil and Sybil fall out over alterations to the hotel (rpt.).
9.40	**FILM:** A Dangerous Summer (see Film Guide).
11.5	**TENNIS:** Benson and Hedges Final.
11.55	**MUSIC AT NIGHT. 12.10 CLOSE.**

CHANNEL 4

1.5	**IRISH ANGLE — HANDS:** Basket Maker.
1.30	**FACE THE PRESS:** Graham Kelly, Secretary of the Football League, questioned by Ian Wooldridge of the Daily Mail and Brian Glanville of the Sunday Times.
2.0	**POB'S PROGRAMME**, with Patricia Hodge.
2.30	**FILM*:** Journey Together (see Film Guide).
4.15	**FILM*:** The London Blackout Murders, with John Abbot (see Film Guide).
5.15	**NEWS; WEATHER,** followed by **THE BUSINESS PROGRAMME.**
6.0	**AMERICAN FOOTBALL:** Dallas Cowboys at Washington Redskins.
7.15	**THE HEART OF THE DRAGON:** Understanding (rpt.).
8.15	**THE JEWEL IN THE CROWN (T):** The Towers of Silence (rpt.).
9.15	**THE WRITING ON THE WALL:** Who Governs? The political events of 1974 recalled by Robert Kee.
10.25	**FILM*:** Seven Days to Noon (see Film Guide). **12.10 CLOSE.**

Exercise 21

1. For how many minutes do each of the following programmes last:
   (a) 'The money programme',
   (b) 'Fawlty Towers',
   (c) 'Face the press',
   (d) '100 great sporting moments'?

2. How much of a video tape would be used if 'The Jewel in the Crown' and 'The writing on the wall' were recorded?

3. At what time does 'Comrades' start on the 24-hour clock?

4. There were four films on the two channels. What was the title of the shortest film?

5. A video tape is 3 hours long. How much of the tape is not used after taping the two films in the afternoon on Channel 4?

6. How much time is devoted to sport on BBC 2? [Include 'Under sail'].

7. For how many hours and minutes does Channel 4 broadcast programmes?

8. What is the starting time on the 24-hour clock of the programme in which 'Basil' appears?

9. How many programmes were repeats?

10. For how long are 'Pages from Ceefax' broadcast?

11. What is the starting time on the 24-hour clock of the programme in which the 'Redskins' appear?

12. How much of a two hour video tape is not used after taping 'Windmill' and 'The Natural World'?

13. For how many hours and minutes does BBC 2 broadcast programmes?

Exercise 22

London to Harrow, Watford, Chesham, Amersham and Aylesbury

Station		BR						BR						BR	
Marylebone		1910						2010						2110	
Baker Street	1850		1905	1920	1933	1935	1950		2005	2020	2033	2035	2050		2105
Finchley Road	1856		1911	1926	1939	1941	1956		2011	2026	2039	2041	2056		2111
Wembley Park	1902		1917	1932		1947	2002		2017	2032		2047	2102		2117
Preston Road	1904		1919	1934		1949	2004		2019	2034		2049	2104		2119
Northwick Park	1907		1922	1937		1952	2007		2022	2037		2052	2107		2122
Harrow-on-the-Hill	1909	1922	1924	1939	1949	1954	2009	2022	2024	2039	2049	2054	2109	2122	2124
North Harrow	1912		1927	1942		1957	2012		2027	2042		2057	2112		2127
Pinner	1914		1929	1944		1959	2014		2029	2044		2059	2114		2129
Northwood Hills ...	1917		1932	1947		2002	2017		2032	2047		2102	2117		2132
Northwood	1920		1935	1950		2005	2020		2035	2050		2105	2120		2135
Moor Park	1923	1930	1938	1953	1957	2008	2023	2030	2038	2053	2057	2108	2123	2130	2138
Croxley	1927		1942	1957		2012	2027		2042	2057		2112	2127		2142
Watford	1933		1947	2003		2017	2033		2047	2103		2117	2133		2147
Rickmansworth	—	1934	—	—	2001			2034	—	—	2101			2134	—
Chorleywood	...	1938	...	...	2005		...	2038	...	...	2105		...	2138	...
Chesham ... dep	...	1928c	...	...	1958c		...	2028c	...	...	2058c		...	2128c	...
Chalfont & Latimer ...	...	1943	...	...	2009		...	2043	...	...	2109		...	2143	...
Chesham ... arr	...	1954c	...	...	2019c		...	2054c	...	...	2119c		...	2154c	...
Amersham	...	1948	...	...	2013		...	2048	...	...	2113		...	2148	...
Great Missenden ...	...	1955	...	...	—		...	2055	...	...	—		...	2155	...•
Wendover	...	2002	...	...	...		...	2102	...	...	...		...	2202	...
Stoke Mandeville ...	...	2006	...	...	...		...	2106	...	...	...		...	2206	...
Aylesbury	...	2010	...	...	...		...	2110	...	...	...		...	2210	...

c   Change at Chalfont & Latimer (journey time from or to Chesham about 9 minutes)
≎   British Rail service with First and Second class accommodation

Copy and complete the table below.

	Depart		Arrive	
1.	Baker Street	1920	Harrow-on-the-Hill	*
2.	Baker Street	2033	Moor Park	*
3.	Pinner	1944	Watford	*
4.	Finchley Road	1856	Pinner	*
5.	Wembley Park	2032	Croxley	*
6.	Preston Road	*	Northwood	1920
7.	Baker Street	*	Chalfont & Latimer	2109
8.	Northwick Park	*	Moor Park	2053
9.	Moor Park	*	Amersham	2013
10.	Chorleywood	*	Wendover	2102
11.	Finchley Road	1856	*	1917
12.	Pinner	2014	*	2033
13.	North Harrow	2112	*	2127
14.	Wembley Park	2117	*	2138
15.	Marylebone	2010	*	2110
16.	*	2039	Chorleywood	2105
17.	*	2022	Stoke Mandeville	2106
18.	*	1942	Watford	2003
19.	*	2049	Croxley	2112
20.	*	1910	Wendover	2002

Exercise 23

Refer to the timetable given in the last exercise.

1. How long does it take the 2050 from Baker Street to get to Watford?

2. How long does it take the 1910 from Marylebone to get to Amersham?

3. How long does it take the British Rail train to go from Marylebone to Harrow-on-the-Hill?

4. How long does it take the British Rail train to go from Harrow-on-the-Hill to Moor Park?

5. Jane leaves home at 1920 and it takes her 15 minutes to walk to Harrow-on-the-Hill station. What is the earliest time at which she can arrive at Watford?

6. Mr Ahmed leaves home at 1945 and it takes him 20 minutes to walk to Wembley Park station. What is the earliest time at which he can arrive at Croxley?

7. Mrs Taylor leaves home at 1920 and it takes her 8 minutes to walk to Finchley Road station. What is the earliest time at which she can arrive at Northwood?

8. Mr Jones must arrive in Watford by 2000. What is the departure time of the latest train he can take from Baker Street?

9. Susan must arrive in Aylesbury by 10 p.m. What is the time of the latest train she can take from Marylebone?

10. Mrs Simpson must arrive in Amersham by 8.30 p.m. What is the time of the latest train she can take from Baker Street?

11. It takes David 25 minutes to drive from home to Marylebone station. He must arrive in Aylesbury by 2130. What is the latest time at which he can leave home?

12. Mrs Perrin takes 15 minutes to walk to Baker Street station from home. She must meet her daughter in Amersham at 2030. What is the latest time at which she can leave home?

13. It takes Louise 18 minutes to walk from home to Moor Park station. She must meet her boyfriend in Amersham at 2130. What is the latest time at which she can leave home?

14. Steve can walk from home to Northwick Park station in 21 minutes. He must meet his brother in Watford at 2020. What is the latest time at which he can leave home?

Part 3

3.1 AREA

Important formulae

Rectangle:
area $= l \times b$

Parallelogram:
area $= b \times h$

Triangle:
area $= \dfrac{b \times h}{2}$

Trapezium:
area $= \left(\dfrac{a + b}{2}\right) h$

Exercise 1

Draw each shape and find its area.

1.

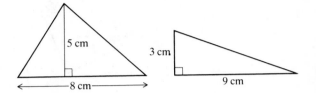

3·2 cm

10 cm

2.

4·2 cm

5 cm

3.

5 cm

8 cm

4.

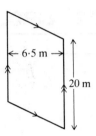

3 cm

9 cm

5.

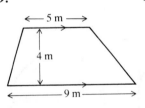

7 cm

4 cm

6.

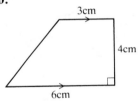

3·8 cm

10 cm

7.

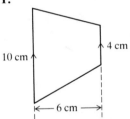

3 m

12 m

8.

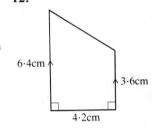

6·5 m

20 m

9.

5 m

4 m

9 m

10.

3cm

4cm

6cm

11.

10 cm

4 cm

6 cm

12.

6·4cm

3·6cm

4·2cm

13.

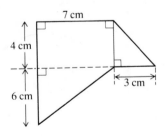

7 cm

4 cm

3 cm

6 cm

14.

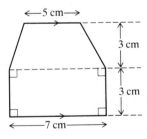

5 cm

3 cm

3 cm

7 cm

In questions **15** to **18** give the answer in 'square units'.

15.

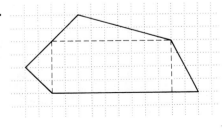

16.

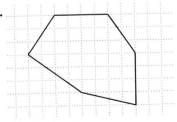

17. Find the shaded area.

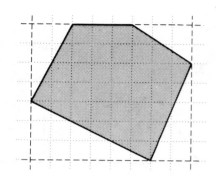

18. Find the shaded area.

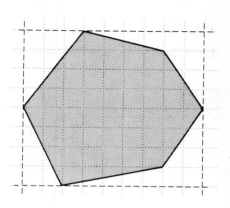

3.2   CIRCLES: CIRCUMFERENCE AND AREA

Find the circumference and area of the circle below.

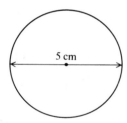

5 cm

Circumference = πd
    = $\pi \times 5$
    = 15.7 cm (3 s.f.)

Area = πr^2
    = $\pi \times 2.5^2$
    =19.6 cm^2 (3 s.f.)

Exercise 2

Use 'π' on a calculator or take $\pi = 3.14$. Give the answers correct to 3 s.f. For each circle find
(a) the circumference
(b) the area.

3.

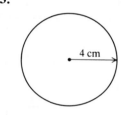

4 cm

4.

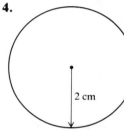

2 cm

5.

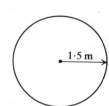

9 m

6.

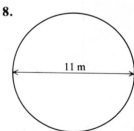

1·5 m

7.

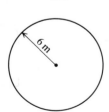

6 m

8.

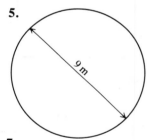

11 m

1.

6 cm

2.

10 cm

9.

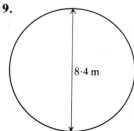

8·4 m

10.

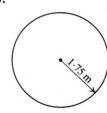

1·75 m

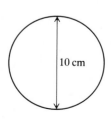

11.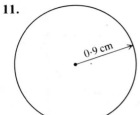

12.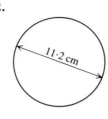

13. Radius = 0.85 cm.
14. Diameter = 7 feet.
15. Diameter = 3.2 km.
16. Radius = 10.1 km.
17. Radius = 0.5 mm.
18. Diameter = $\frac{1}{2}$ mile.
19. Radius = 6.3 km.
20. Diameter = $1\frac{1}{2}$ miles.

More complicated shapes

For the shape below find

(a) the perimeter,
(b) the area.

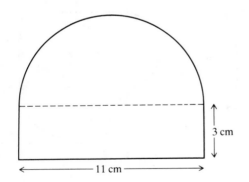

(a) Perimeter = $\left(\dfrac{\pi \times 11}{2}\right) + 11 + 3 + 3$

   = 34.3 cm (3 s.f.)

(b) Area = $\left(\dfrac{\pi \times 5.5^2}{2}\right) + (11 \times 3)$

   = 80.5 cm² (3 s.f.)

Exercise 3

Use the 'π' button on a calculator or take
π = 3.14. Give the answers correct to 3 s.f.
For each shape find (a) the perimeter,
                              (b) the area.

1.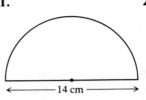

2.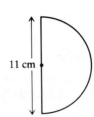

3.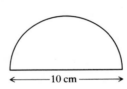

4.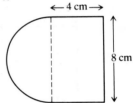

5.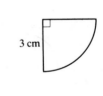

6.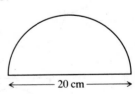

7.

8.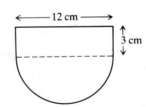

9.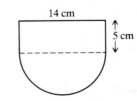

10.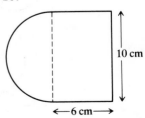

11.

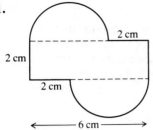

2 cm

2 cm

2 cm

6 cm

12.

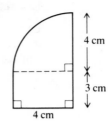

4 cm

3 cm

4 cm

13.

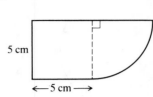

5 cm

5 cm

Exercise 4

This exercise is more difficult. Find the area of each shape. If the area is shaded find the shaded area. Give your answers to 3 s.f.

1.

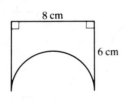

8 cm

6 cm

2.

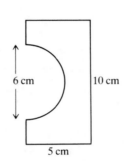

6 cm

10 cm

5 cm

3.

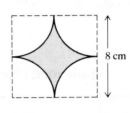

8 cm

4.

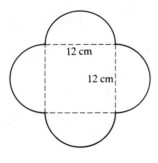

12 cm

12 cm

5.

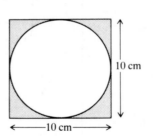

10 cm

10 cm

6.

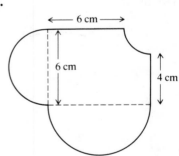

6 cm

6 cm

4 cm

7.

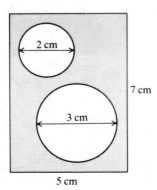

2 cm

7 cm

3 cm

5 cm

8.

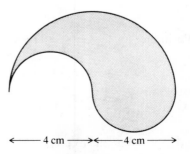

4 cm   4 cm

Finding the radius of a circle

(a) The circumference of a circle is 60 cm.
Find the radius of the circle.

$$C = \pi d$$

$$\therefore 60 = \pi d$$

$$\therefore \frac{60}{\pi} = d$$

$$\therefore r = \frac{(60/\pi)}{2} = 9.55 \text{ cm (to 3 s.f.)}$$

(b) The area of a circle is 18 m². Find the
radius of the circle.

$$\pi r^2 = 18$$

$$r^2 = \frac{18}{\pi}$$

$$r = \sqrt{\left(\frac{18}{\pi}\right)} = 2.39 \text{ m (to 3 s.f.)}$$

Exercise 5

In each question, use the information given to
calculate the radius of the circle. Use the 'π'
button on a calculator or take π = 3.14.

1. The circumference is 15 cm
2. The circumference is 28 m
3. The circumference is 7 m
4. The circumference is 40 cm
5. The area is 54 cm²
6. The area is 38 cm²
7. The area is 49 m²
8. The area is 28 m²
9. The circumference is 16 m
10. The area is 60 cm²
11. The circumference is 29 cm
12. The circumference is 35 m
13. The area is 104 cm²
14. The area is 70 cm²
15. The circumference is 22 m
16. The circumference is 56 cm
17. The area is 52 m²
18. The area is 44 cm²
19. The circumference is 18 m
20. The circumference is 25 cm
21. The area is 30 cm²
22. The circumference is 30 cm
23. The area is 64 m²
24. The area is 80 cm²
25. The circumference is 33 m

Exercise 6

1. The circumference of a circle is 52 m. Find
   its area.
2. The circumference of a circle is 35 cm. Find
   its area.
3. The area of a circle is 61 cm². Find its
   circumference.
4. The area of a circle is 29 m². Find its
   circumference.
5. The circumference of a circle is 48 cm. Find
   its area.
6. The area of a circle is 100 cm². Find its
   circumference.
7. The area of a circle is 86 m². Find its
   circumference.
8. The circumference of a circle is 14 m. Find
   its area.
9. The area of a circle is 72 m². Find its
   circumference.
10. The circumference of a circle is 25 m. Find
    its area.
11. The circumference of a circle is 61 cm. Find
    its area.
12. The area of a circle is 40 cm². Find its
    circumference.
13. The circumference of a circle is 40 cm. Find
    its area.
14. The area of a circle is 32.5 m². Find its
    circumference.
15. The circumference of a circle is 46.5 cm.
    Find its area.
16. The circumference of a circle is 12.6 cm.
    Find its area.

Exercise 7

1. A rectangle has an area of 54 cm² and a
   length of 6 cm. Find its breadth.
2. A rectangle has an area of 60 cm² and a
   length of 8 cm. Find its breadth.
3. Find the area of a rectangle with a perimeter
   of 26 cm and a side of 8 cm.
4. Find the area of a rectangle with a perimeter
   of 29 cm and a side of 10 cm.
5. Find the perimeter of a rectangle with an
   area of 55 cm² and a side of 10 cm.
6. Find the perimeter of a square with an area
   of 144 cm².

7. In the diagram below find
(a) the area of rectangle ABCD,
(b) the area of triangle DTC.
[Give answers in square units.]

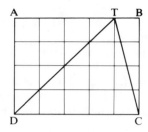

8. Each of the sides of three different rectangles is a whole number of centimetres. Each rectangle has an area of 12 cm², but each has a different perimeter. Draw a diagram to show each of the rectangles.

9. The diagram below shows a rectangular wooden door measuring 2 m by 0.9 m in which a rectangular glass window measuring 1.2 m by 0.6 m has been fitted.

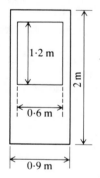

Find, in square metres,
(a) the area of glass,
(b) the area of wood.

10. A running track has two semicircular ends of radius 34 m and two straights of 93.2 m as shown below.

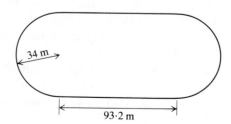

(a) Calculate the total distance around the track.
(b) Find the extra distance travelled per lap by a runner who runs 1 m outside the line all the way round.

11. The diagram shows a square ABCD in which DX = XY = YC = AW. The area of the square is 45 cm².

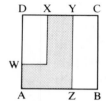

(a) What is the fraction $\frac{DX}{DC}$?
(b) What fraction of the square is shaded?
(c) Find the area of the unshaded part.

12. The diagram below shows a lawn (unshaded) surrounded by a path of uniform width (shaded). The curved end of the lawn is a semi-circle of diameter 10 m.

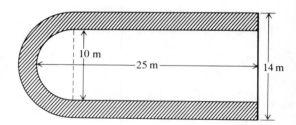

Calculate:
(a) the length of the rectangular part of the lawn,
(b) the area of this rectangular part of the lawn,
(c) the area of the semi-circular part of the lawn,
(d) the area of each rectangular part of the path,
(e) the area of the curved part of the path,
(f) the total area of the path.

13. Calculate the shaded area below.

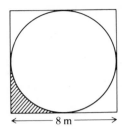

8 m

14. How many complete revolutions does a cycle wheel of diameter 60 cm make in travelling 400 m?

15. How many complete revolutions does a car wheel of diameter 70 cm make in travelling 600 m?

16. A sheet of metal measures 60 cm by 20 cm. It is melted down and recast into discs of the same thickness and radius 5 cm. How many complete discs will be cast?

17. A circular duck pond has an area of 65 m². Find the radius of the pond.

18. A circular wheel makes 50 complete revolutions in travelling a distance of 100 m. Find the diameter of the wheel.

3.3   VOLUME AND SURFACE AREA

Important formulae

Cuboid : $V = l \times b \times h$
Prism : $V = A \times l$
Cylinder : $V = \pi r^2 h$
Sphere : $V = \frac{4}{3}\pi r^3$
Cone : $V = \frac{1}{3}\pi r^2 h$
Pyramid : $V = \frac{1}{3}$ (base area) × height.

Exercise 8

1. Find the volume

(a)

(b)

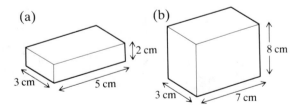

(a) 2 cm, 3 cm, 5 cm
(b) 8 cm, 3 cm, 7 cm

2. Find the length x.

(a)

(b)

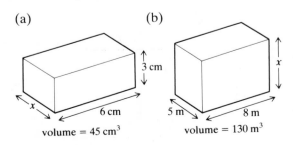

(a) x, 6 cm, volume = 45 cm³
(b) 3 cm, x, 5 m, 8 m, volume = 130 m³

3. Copy and complete the table. All the objects are cuboids.

	length	breadth	height	volume
(a)	3 cm	3 cm	2 cm	
(b)	7 cm	4 cm	$\frac{1}{2}$ cm	
(c)	10 cm	8.5 cm	2 cm	
(d)	6 cm		3 cm	90 cm³
(e)	8 cm		3 cm	144 cm³
(f)	5 cm		6 cm	45 cm³
(g)	7 cm	6 cm		147 cm³
(h)	9 cm	3 cm		297 cm³
(i)	8 cm	4 cm		6.4 cm³
(j)		8 cm	3 cm	54 cm³
(k)		0.2 cm	0.6 cm	0.012 cm³
(l)	6 cm	5 cm		72 cm³
(m)		7 cm	6 cm	357 cm³
(n)	8 cm		5 cm	284 cm³

4. A rectangular block of metal has dimensions 20 cm × 16 cm × 8 cm. It is melted down and recast into cubes of edge length 4 cm. How many cubes will be cast?

5. A freezer makes ice cubes which are rectangular blocks 5 cm × 3 cm × 2 cm. How many ice cubes can be made from 3 litres of water?

6. A wall, 12 m long, 150 cm high and 15 cm thick is constructed using bricks which are 20 cm × 15 cm × 10 cm. How many bricks are needed (ignore the cement).

Exercise 9

Find the volume of each of the solid objects below. Give the answers correct to 3 s.f.

1.

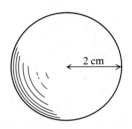
2 cm

2.

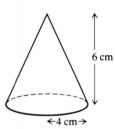
8 cm
3 cm

3.

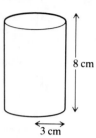
6 cm
←4 cm→

4.

3·2 cm

5.

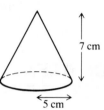
7 cm
5 cm

6.

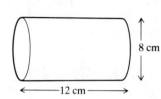
8 cm
12 cm

7.

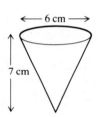
← 6 cm →
7 cm

8.

2·1 cm

9.

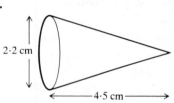
2·2 cm
4·5 cm

10.

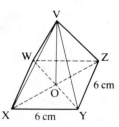
2 cm

11.

1·4 cm

12.

0·9 cm

13.

V
W   Z
6 cm
O
X   6 cm   Y

WX = XY = YZ = WZ
    = 6 cm
VO = 5 cm

14.

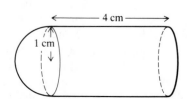
V
A   D
O
B   C

AB = DC = 3 cm
BC = AD = 6 cm
VO = 5 cm

The objects in questions
15 and **16** consist of cones,
cylinders and hemispheres
joined together.

15.

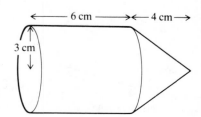
← 4 cm →
1 cm

16.

← 6 cm →← 4 cm →
3 cm

Exercise 10

Use 'π' on a calculator or take π = 3.14. Give answers correct to 3 S.F.

1. Find the capacity in litres of the oil drum shown below. (1000 cm^3 = 1 litre).

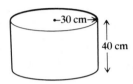

2. Find the volume in litres of a cylinder of height 55 cm and diameter 20 cm.

3. The two objects shown below are made of the same material. Which is the heavier?

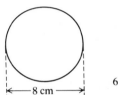

4. A washing powder is sold in two sizes, a giant size for £2.05 and a standard size for 90p

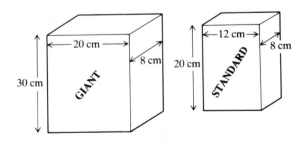

   (a) (i) Calculate the volume of the standard size packet.
        (ii) Calculate the volume of the giant size packet.
   (b) It takes 2½ packets of standard size to fill the giant size.
        (i) Calculate the cost of 2 standard size packets and half a packet (at half standard-size price).
        (ii) Which is cheaper, a giant packet or 2½ standard packets?
        (iii) How much is saved?

5. Calculate the volume of the object below.

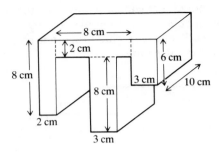

6. A solid sphere of radius 2 cm is melted down and recast into a number of discs of radius 1 cm and thickness 0.2 cm. Calculate
   (a) the volume of the sphere,
   (b) the volume of one disc,
   (c) the number of complete discs which can be made from the sphere.

7. Liquid is poured into an inverted cone of internal radius 10 cm and height 15 cm at a rate of 6 cm^3/s. How long will it take to fill the cone?

8. Cylinders are cut along the axis of symmetry to form the objects below. Find the volume of each object.

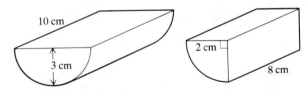

9. The diagram below shows a cross section through the centre of a hollow spherical ball made of steel.

   Calculate
   (a) the volume of steel used to make the ball,
   (b) the weight of the ball if the density of steel is 8 g/cm^3.

Exercise 11

1. The solid object shown below is made from 27 small cubes each 1 cm by 1 cm by 1 cm. The small cubes are glued together and then the outside is painted red.

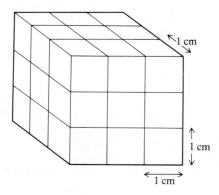

(b)

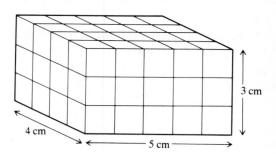

Calculate
(a) the number of cubes with one face painted
(b) the number of cubes with two faces painted
(c) the number of cubes with three faces painted
(d) the number of cubes with no faces painted

(Check that the answers to (a), (b), (c) and (d) add up to the correct number.)

(c)

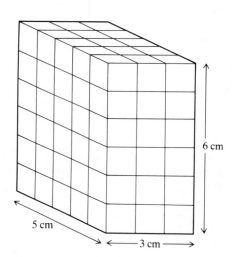

2. Repeat question **1** for the solid objects shown below, each of which is made from 1 cm cubes.

(a)

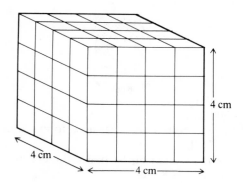

(d)

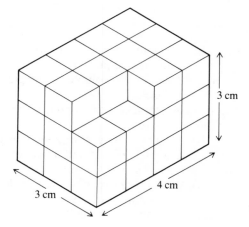

3.4   NETS AND SOLIDS

If the cube below was made of cardboard, and you cut along some of the edges and laid it out flat, you would have the *net* of the cube.

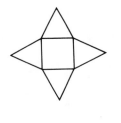

cube   net

Here is the net for a square-based pyramid.

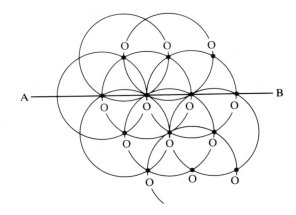

Exercise 12

In question **1** we will construct a series of equilateral triangles using a ruler and a pair of compasses.

1. (a) Draw a straight line AB and draw a pattern of circles of radius 3 cm as shown. The centres of the circles are marked with an O.

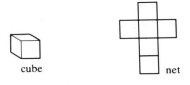

(b) Draw the lines through the O's to produce a series of equilateral triangles.

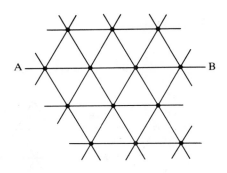

(c) We can also see a series of regular hexagons in the pattern above.

In questions **2** to **5** objects are shown, together with the net which will produce them. Draw the net on a piece of cardboard using the method from question **1**. Cut out the net and fold it to make the object.

2. Tetrahedron

net:

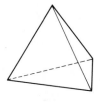

3. Octahedron

net:

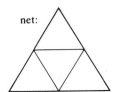

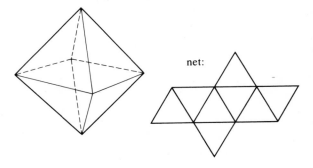

4. Icosahedron (20 faces)

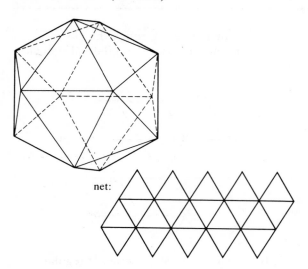

net: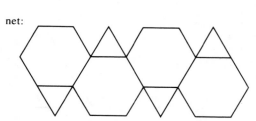

5. Truncated tetrahedron

net:

Use the circle pattern method to draw the net of hexagons and equilateral triangles.

6. A cube dissected into three pyramids. Make three solids from the net shown. They can be fitted together to form a cube. This demonstrates the formula for the volume of a pyramid.

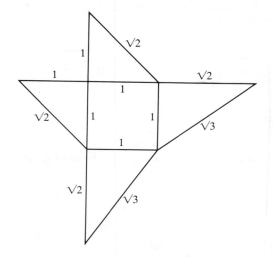

7. Which of the nets below can be used to make a cube?

(a)   (b)

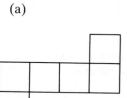   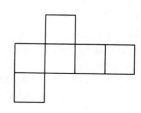

(c)   (d)

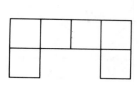   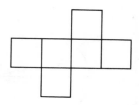

Think about it   1

Project 1	MATHEMATICAL WORDSEARCH

Copy the square below. Find as many mathematical words as possible and make a list.

The words appear written forwards or backwards in any row, column or diagonal.

A	P	M	N	C	I	R	C	L	E	V	Z
E	O	E	D	I	V	I	D	E	B	Q	E
L	R	A	D	I	U	S	R	V	R	T	Q
G	E	T	U	C	A	H	L	M	A	S	U
N	Q	L	N	A	T	M	U	N	C	U	A
A	U	O	L	B	V	L	I	U	K	M	T
P	A	R	N	A	T	D	T	O	E	E	I
Q	L	J	U	I	R	D	F	P	T	R	O
R	M	C	P	O	S	A	X	I	S	T	N
W	K	L	O	G	F	H	P	D	E	N	I
T	Y	C	A	L	C	U	L	A	T	E	Q
L	R	E	T	E	M	A	I	D	R	X	S

Your rating: 10 Average
                  15 Good
                  20 Very good
   More than 20 Excellent

Exercise A

1. A television programme lasting 2 hours 15 minutes finishes at 21 50. At what time does the film start?

2. How much change from £10 should I receive after spending £2.07?

3. It costs £8 to join a tennis club and 80p for each game. Calculate the total cost of joining the club and then playing 20 games.

4. Work out $\frac{2}{5} \times \frac{3}{4}$, giving your answer in its simplest form.

5. Calculate the area of the shape below.

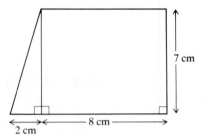

6. The bill for 8 people in a restaurant is £61.60. Find the cost per person correct to the nearest pound.

7. A mechanic is paid £4.80 per hour for normal time and overtime is paid at time and a half. How much does he earn in a week when he works 40 hours normal time and 8 hours overtime?

8. The diagram shows the plan view of a room which is 2.5 m in height.

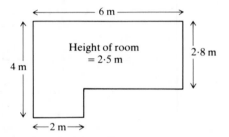

Emulsion paint costs £3.40 per litre.
1 litre of paint covers 7 m².
Copy and complete the following table.

Perimeter of room	m
Total area of all walls	m²
Area of doors and windows	15 m²
Area which requires painting	m²
Number of litres of paint needed for 2 coats	
Cost of paint	£

9. A man owed £150. How much does he owe after making payments of £45.50, £27 and £51?

10. The mileometer of a car shows a reading of 14 941 miles. This number is called 'palindromic' because it reads the same backwards or forwards.
   (a) What will be the reading when the next palindromic number appears?
   (b) How far will the car have travelled by then?

Project 2   CROSSNUMBERS WITHOUT CLUES

Here we have four crossnumbers with no clues, only the answers. Copy the patterns shown and then fill in the answers by working 'backwards'.

1. Copy the pattern below.

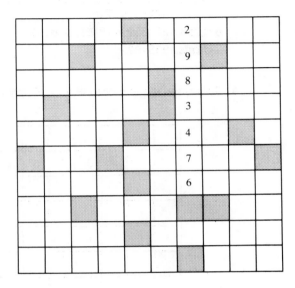

The answers are below. One number has been put in to help you get started. It is a good idea to copy out a list of all the answers so that you can tick them off as you put them onto the pattern.

2 digits: 13, 22, 28, 45, 74, 91, 93, 97.

3 digits: 236, 252, 276, 448, 669, 962.

4 digits: 1219, 2414, 3180, 3436, 3746, 4105, 4254, 5093, 5231, 5636, 8313.

5 digits: 11060, 15283, 16283, 19870, 26105, 35368, 37852, 51273, 60757, 78787, 92523.

6 digits: 191800, 401915, 403645.

7 digits: 2983476.✓

2. Copy the same pattern as for question **1** (without the 2983476). Here are the answers:

2 digits: 15, 22, 23, 23, 24, 26, 31, 81.

3 digits: 126, 127, 356, 357, 414, 651.

4 digits: 1358, 1364, 1527, 2158, 3214, 3216, 3416, 3789, 4177, 5427, 6500.

5 digits: 21011, 24629, 36973, 37189, 45189, 48211, 53636, 64285, 71820, 95890, 97215.

6 digits: 582355, 652748, 653648.

7 digits: 4413516.

3. Copy the same pattern as for question **1** (without the 2983476).
Here are the answers:

2 digits: 28, 56, 66, 67, 68, 88, 92, 93.

3 digits: 171, 372, 387, 415, 485, 675.

4 digits: 1583, 1613, 1683, 2319, 3214, 3217, 3218, 3248, 5218, 8131, 9635.

5 digits: 26561, 26852, 26895, 60911, 60918, 68812, 74164, 82103, 82777, 84266, 91718.

6 digits: 252852, 428151, 448161.

7 digits: 8339822.

4. This question is more difficult. Copy the pattern below.

			3	7	3	8					
3	1	1	8								
6											
7											
										4

2 digits 13, 16, 19, 49, 60, 63, 65, 68, 74, 84, 85.

3 digits: 168, 316, 516, 610, 616, 617, 735, 785, 801, 815, 833, 885, 928.

4 digits: 3118, 3218, 3738, 5524, 6815, 7516, 7816, 7826, 7856.

5 digits: 21748, 21758, 53674, 53681, 63117, 63546, 63576, 63588, 63781, 63881, 76293, 78151, 92505.

6 digits: 639669, 813849.

7 digits: 3896152.

Exercise B

1. The cash price of a television is £320. It can be bought on hire purchase by paying a deposit of £65 and 24 monthly payments of £12.50. Calculate the total cost of buying the television on hire purchase.

2. A man earns £5980 per annum. How much is this per week?

3. It takes 20 minutes per lb plus an extra 15 minutes to cook a duck. At what time would you put a 9 lb duck into the oven if you wish to have it ready at 1.30 p.m.?

4. What change do you receive from £10 after buying 6 pens at 22p, 4 sharpeners at 32p and 5 pencils at 8p?

5. Two numbers x and t are such that t is greater than 6 and x is less than 4. Arrange the numbers 5, t and x in order of size, starting with the smallest.

6. To the nearest whole number 5.84, 16.23 and 7.781 are 6, 16 and 8 respectively.
   (a) Use these approximate values to obtain an approximate result for $\dfrac{5.84 \times 16.23}{7.781}$

   (b) Use the same approach to obtain approximate results for

   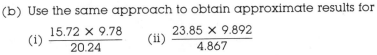

   (i) $\dfrac{15.72 \times 9.78}{20.24}$ (ii) $\dfrac{23.85 \times 9.892}{4.867}$

7. King Richard is given three coins which look identical, but in fact one of them is an overweight fake. Describe how he could discover the fake using an ordinary balance and only *one* weighing operation.

8. How many hours are there in February 1987?

9. A cup can be filled fifty times from 18 litres of milk. What is the capacity of the cup in cm^3. ($1000\ cm^3 = 1$ litre).

10. A pile of 400 sheets of paper is 2.5 cm thick. What is the thickness in cm of one sheet of paper?

Project 3   SPOTTED SHAPES

For this investigation you need dotted paper. If you have not got any you can make your own using a felt tip pen and squared paper.

In Figure 1 there are 10 dots on the perimeter ($p = 10$) and 2 dots inside the shape ($i = 2$). The area of the shape is 6 square units ($A = 6$).

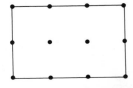

Figure 1

In Figure 2 there are 14 dots on the perimeter ($p = 14$) and 6 dots inside the shape ($i = 6$). The area of the shape is 12 square units ($A = 12$).

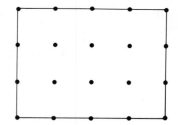

Figure 2

Draw the shapes below and record the values for p, i and A in a table like the one shown.

p	i	A	leave a space
10	2	6	
14	6	12	

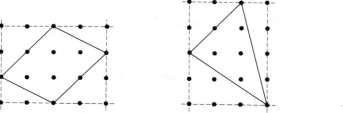

Draw more shapes of your own design and record the results in the table. Include some more difficult shapes like those below.

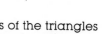

The area of the shape is found by subtracting the areas of the triangles from the area of the surrounding rectangle (shown with a broken line).

In the space you left in the table of results, work out the value of $(\frac{1}{2}p + i)$ for each shape.

Is there a formula connecting p, i and A?

Draw further shapes, even more complicated, to check your formula.

Exercise C   **OPERATOR SQUARES**

Each empty square contains either a number or a mathematical symbol ($+$, $-$, $\times$, $\div$). Copy each square and fill in the missing details.

1.

11		4	$\rightarrow$	15
$\times$		$\div$		
		2	$\rightarrow$	3
$\downarrow$		$\downarrow$		
66			$\rightarrow$	132

2.

9		17	$\rightarrow$	26
$\times$		$-$		
5	$\times$		$\rightarrow$	
$\downarrow$		$\downarrow$		
	$\div$	9	$\rightarrow$	5

3.

14	$+$		$\rightarrow$	31
$\times$				
4		23	$\rightarrow$	92
$\downarrow$		$\downarrow$		
	$-$	40	$\rightarrow$	

4.

15			$\rightarrow$	5
$+$		$\times$		
		5	$\rightarrow$	110
$\downarrow$		$\downarrow$		
	$-$	15	$\rightarrow$	22

5.

	$\times$	10	$\rightarrow$	90
$+$		$\div$		
			$\rightarrow$	$5\frac{1}{2}$
$\downarrow$		$\downarrow$		
20	$\times$		$\rightarrow$	100

6.

	$\times$		$\rightarrow$	52
$-$		$\times$		
	$\times$	4	$\rightarrow$	
$\downarrow$		$\downarrow$		
8		8	$\rightarrow$	1

7.

5			$\rightarrow$	60
$\times$		$\div$		
		24	$\rightarrow$	44
$\downarrow$		$\downarrow$		
	$\times$	$\frac{1}{2}$	$\rightarrow$	50

8.

	$\times$	6	$\rightarrow$	42
$\div$		$\div$		
14	$-$		$\rightarrow$	
$\downarrow$		$\downarrow$		
		2	$\rightarrow$	1

9.

	$\times$	2	$\rightarrow$	38
$-$		$\div$		
			$\rightarrow$	48
$\downarrow$		$\downarrow$		
7	$-$		$\rightarrow$	$6\frac{1}{2}$

10.

17	$\times$		$\rightarrow$	170
$-$		$\div$		
	$\div$		$\rightarrow$	
$\downarrow$		$\downarrow$		
8	$-$	0·1	$\rightarrow$	

11.

0·3	$\times$	20	$\rightarrow$	
		$-$		
11	$\div$		$\rightarrow$	
$\downarrow$		$\downarrow$		
11·3	$-$		$\rightarrow$	2·3

12.

	$\times$	50	$\rightarrow$	25
$-$		$\div$		
		$\frac{1}{2}$	$\rightarrow$	0·6
$\downarrow$		$\downarrow$		
0·4	$\times$		$\rightarrow$	

13.

7	×		→	0·7
÷		×		
	÷		→	
↓		↓		
1·75	+	0·02	→	

14.

	+	8	→	9·4
−				
	×	0·1	→	
↓		↓		
1·3		0·8	→	2·1

15.

	×		→	30
−				
	÷	10	→	0·25
↓		↓		
97·5	+	3	→	

16.

3	÷	2	→	
÷		÷		
8	÷		→	
↓		↓		
	+	$\frac{1}{8}$	→	

17.

	−	$\frac{1}{16}$	→	$\frac{3}{16}$
×				
	÷	4	→	
↓		↓		
$\frac{1}{8}$		$\frac{1}{4}$	→	$\frac{3}{8}$

18.

0·5	−	0·01	→	
			×	
	×		→	35
↓		↓		
4	÷	0·1	→	

Project 4   NUMBER MESSAGES

(a) Start at the box containing the letter 'Q'.
(b) Work out the answer to the question in the box.
(c) Look for the answer in the corner of another box.
(d) Write down the letter in the box and then work out the answer to the problem in the box.
(e) Look for the answer as before and continue until you arrive back at box 'Q'.
(f) Read the message.

1.

147 **Q** 15 + 19	153 **D** 21 × 7	101 **R** 200 − 47	42 **V** 26 + 98
124 **E** 22 × 3	91 **I** 20 × 6	34 **M** 5 × 15	36 **A** 11 + 90
63 **H** 11 × 11	66 **R** 84 ÷ 4	21 **Y** 110 − 70	81 **T** 36 + 27
75 **A** 100 − 19	40 **H** 216 ÷ 6	121 **S** 95 − 4	120 **S** 61 − 19

2.

27 **Q** $99 - 27$	99 **S** $2212 \div 7$	125 **W** $211 - 99$	444 **N** 110×9
766 **I** $(18 - 13)^2$	112 **O** $(21 - 18)^3$	615 **N** 18×20	25 **S** $108 + 209$
317 **T** $625 \div 5$	990 **E** $840 \div 3$	72 **O** $123 + 321$	118 **U** $3^2 \times 11$
166 **L** $19 + 99$	360 **E** $1000 - 234$	316 **O** $5 + 55 + 555$	280 **P** $200 - 34$

3.

0.42 **Q** $8.1 + 5$	3.3 **R** $6.1 \div 5$	4.1 **B** $19 - 13.7$	10.5 **R** $14.5 - 3$
5.3 **I** $3.24 \div 9$	11.5 **S** $0.84 \div 4$	1.22 **E** $11 - 8.95$	0.01 **H** 4.2×0.1
2.05 **R** 0.313×100	31.3 **U** $8.8 + 9.9$	13.1 **S** $8 - 3.7$	0.21 **A** 0.33×10
4.3 **P** $2.4 + 7$	0.36 **S** $10 - 9.99$	18.7 **B** 8.2×0.5	9.4 **U** 2.1×5

4.

6 **Q** $10 + 3 \times 2$	13 **S** $22 + 20 \div 10$	33 **R** $19 - 12 \div 6$	71 **N** $7 \times 4 - 15 \div 5$
7 **E** $8 + 9 \div 3$	53 **O** $39 - 17 \times 2$	25 **D** $(25 + 23) \div 8$	19 **E** $13 - 3 \times 2$
55 **H** $2 \times 3 + 4 \times 2$	5 **U** $8 \times 7 + 3 \times 5$	16 **T** $12 - 4 \times 2$	17 **T** $(4 + 7) \times 5$
4 **H** $6 \times 3 + 1$	24 **R** $3 \times 14 + 11$	14 **I** $3 \times 5 - 1 \times 2$	11 **A** $5 \times 7 - 2$

5.

50 **Q** $2.5 \times 4 + 3$	8.1 **O** $5 \times 9 - 2 \times 9$	2.13 **N** $7 - 0.04 \times 10$	2 **N** $0.5 \times 2 + 17$
7.2 **L** $0.3 \times 100 - 7$	3.5 **O** $8 \times 5 + 6 \times 7$	84 **G** $11 \times 9 - 7 \times 7$	52.2 **G** $10 \times (3.4 + 5)$
6 **A** $1.7 + 3 \div 10$	23 **A** $13 \div 100 + 2$	13 **C** $8 - 0.2 \times 10$	7.24 **B** $8 + 1 \div 10$
82 **U** $6.2 \div 5 + 6$	27 **I** $8 - 0.4 \times 2$	6.6 **E** $3.2 + 7 \times 7$	18 **Y** $12.5 - 3 \times 3$

6.

-13 **Q** $- 6 + 2$	-7 **C** $(-3)^2 + 4^2$	12 **Y** $12 \div (-2)$	0 **A** $12 \times (-10)$	-14 **A** $- 8 + 17$
-120 **R** $16 \div (-16)$	-8 **H** $- 3 - 15$	-18 **E** $(-2)^2$	8 **E** $(-8) \div (-8)$	4 **R** $- 3 + 7 - 9$
-6 **T** $- 8 - 9$	13 **E** $- 2 + 1 - 1$	-4 **M** $(-3) \times (-4)$	25 **L** $- 7 + 20$	1 **R** $- 3 - 2 - 8$
9 **C** $(-8) \div 1$	-5 **S** $0 \times (-17)$	-2 **V** $6 - (-2)$	-1 **E** $- 2 + 6 - 11$	-17 **E** $- 2 \times 7$

7.

3.62 **Q** $12 - 8.99$	8 **O** $45 \div 9 - 5$	25 **U** $90 \times 2 - 5$	300 **S** $- 8 - 6$	1.3 **L** $6 + 9 \div 3$
-9 **A** 2.6×0.5	6 **Y** $0.7 \div 100$	0.27 **R** $(-1)^2 + (-2)^2$	21 **N** $200 - 41$	159 **G** $25.34 \div 7$
0 **R** $1.4 + 19$	1.24 **A** $9 \times 5 - 3 \times 7$	3.01 **M** $18 - 3 \times 4$	5 **O** $6 \times (11 - 7.5)$	175 **L** $6.2 \div 5$
9 **C** $(-2)^2 + 21$	-14 **W** 2.7×0.1	20.4 **I** 0.3×1000	24 **T** $- 7 + 15$	0.007 **C** $-36 \div 4$

Exercise D

1. Eight litres of wine cost £12. Find the cost of 15 litres of the wine.

2. Write correct to the nearest pound:
  (a) £57.80   (b) £62.45   (c) £124.85
  (d) £6.781   (e) £11.382   (f) £567.60

3. A wooden box when empty weighs 5.2 kg. It contains: 5 tins each weighing 400 g; 7 jars each weighing 675 g; 10 bags each weighing 225 g and 2 bottles each weighing 1050 g. Find the total weight of the box and its contents.

4. A lawnmower has a blade 2 m wide. A groundsman has to cut the grass on a playing surface 100 m by 60 m. He cuts up and down the length of the field.
  (a) How many times does he push the mower the length of the field?
  (b) What area of grass does he cut each time?

5. Twenty articles cost £50. How many of these articles could be bought for £7.50?

6. How many apples at 16p each would be a fair exchange for 48 oranges costing 11p each?

7. A saleswoman is paid a basic salary of £4200 per year, plus commission of 4% on all her sales. Calculate her total salary if her sales totalled
  (a) £10 000   (b) £30 000   (c) £100 000.

8. Peter walks at $4\frac{1}{2}$ km/h and he cycles three times as fast. How long will he take to cycle $33\frac{3}{4}$ km?

9. If we require an estimate of 82 × 43, to the nearest thousand, we may say 82 × 43 ≈ 80 × 40
$$= 3200$$
$$= 3000 \text{ to the nearest thousand.}$$
Use this method to estimate the value of the following, to the nearest thousand.
  (a) 71 × 69   (b) 998 × 41   (c) 11 × 607   (d) 497 × 206

10. Change the fractions $\frac{5}{8}$ and $\frac{7}{11}$ into decimals. Which fraction is larger?

Project 5   THINK OF A NUMBER

Ask someone to follow these instructions:

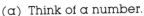

(a) Think of a number.
(b) Add 11 to the number.
(c) Multiply the answer by 5.
(d) Subtract 7 from the new number.
(e) Double the answer.
(f) Add 4 to the last number.
(g) Read out the final answer.

You can now work out the original number as follows:
'Subtract 100 and divide by 10'.
(e.g. If the final answer is 250, the original number was (250 − 100) ÷ 10. It was 15).

Exercise E

1. Write down the next five lines in this pattern.

$1 \times 999 = 999$
$2 \times 999 = 1998$
$3 \times 999 = 2997$
$4 \times 999 = 3996$

2. Copy the pattern and write down the next four lines.

$1 + 9 \times 0 \quad = \quad 1$
$2 + 9 \times 1 \quad = \quad 11$
$3 + 9 \times 12 \quad = \quad 111$
$4 + 9 \times 123 \quad = 1111$
$5 + 9 \times 1234 =$

3. Copy the pattern and write down the next five lines.

$1 \times 9 - 1 = \quad 8$
$21 \times 9 - 1 = \quad 188$
$321 \times 9 - 1 = \quad 2888$
$4321 \times 9 - 1 = 38888$

4. (a) Write down the next four lines of this pattern.

$1^3 = \quad 1^2 \quad = 1$
$1^3 + 2^3 = \quad (1 + 2)^2 \quad = 9$
$1^3 + 2^3 + 3^3 = (1 + 2 + 3)^2 = 36$

(b) Work out as simply as possible
$1^3 + 2^3 + 3^3 + 4^3 + 5^3 + 6^3 + 7^3 + 8^3 + 9^3 + 10^3$.

5. (a) Write down the next three lines of this pattern.

$(1.5)^2 = (1 \times 2) + 0.25$
$(2.5)^2 = (2 \times 3) + 0.25$
$(3.5)^2 = (3 \times 4) + 0.25$

(b) Copy and complete.
$(9.5)^2 = (\quad\quad) +$
$(15.5)^2 = (\quad\quad) +$
$(99.5)^2 = \quad\quad\quad +$

6. Write down the next five lines of this pattern.

$1 = \quad 1 = 1^3$
$3 + \quad 5 = \quad 8 = 2^3$
$7 + \quad 9 + 11 = 27 = 3^3$
$13 + 15 + 17 + 19 = \quad =$

7. Each diagram in the sequence below consists of a number of dots.

Diagram number	1	2	3

(a) Draw diagram number 4, diagram number 5 and diagram number 6.

(b) Copy and complete the table below:

Diagram number	Number of dots
1	6
2	10
3	
4	
5	
6	

(c) Without drawing the diagrams, state the number of dots in
    (i) diagram number 10
    (ii) diagram number 15
    (iii) diagram number 50

(d) State the number of the diagram which has
    (i) 50 dots
    (ii) 162 dots

(e) If we write x for the diagram number and n for the number of dots, write down a formula involving x and n.

Project 6   ESTIMATING

(a) Draw a large copy of table A.

Table A

145	441	609	2059	4260	300
1421	969	45	2940	189	459
540	355	399	639	551	261
95	171	1260	1029	105	1071
1740	3060	245	931	2499	255
1140	3621	1479	3479	1349	1491

Table B

5	21	51
9	29	60
19	49	71

(b) Two players take it in turn to select a pair of numbers from table B and divide them on a calculator. If the answer is in table A and if the number is not yet crossed out the player crosses out that square with a coloured pencil.

(c) The winner is the first player to cross out four squares in a line, either in a column or a row or a diagonal.

Exercise F

Write down the following electricity meter readings. Note the number that the pointer has just passed.

1.

2.

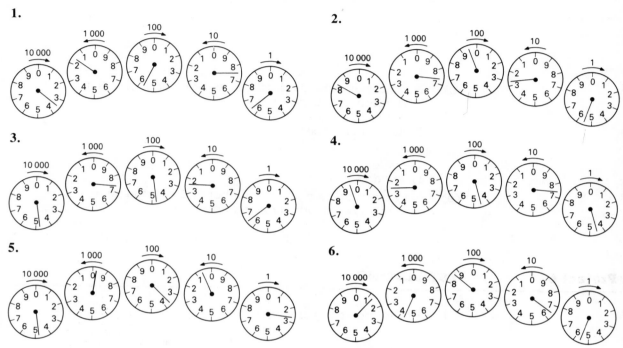

3.

4.

5.

6.

In questions **7**, **8** and **9** find how many units are consumed between each pair of readings.

7.(a)   (b)

8. (a)   (b)

9. (a)   (b)

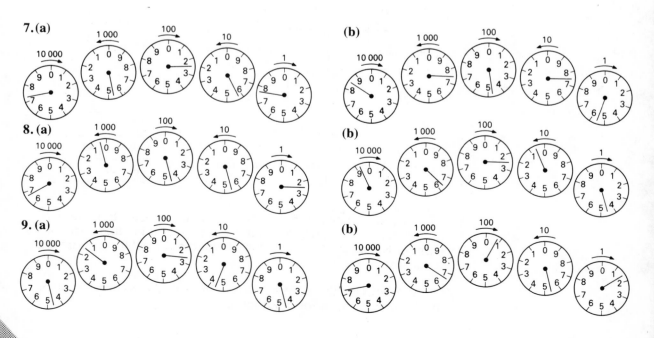

Project 7 BUCKETS

John has two buckets.
One holds 5 litres and
the other holds 8 litres.

He also has a large tank
with a tap.

(a) Suppose he needs exactly 18 litres of water. This is easy. He fills the 5 litre bucket twice and the 8 litre bucket once and pours all the water into the tank.

(b) Suppose he needs 7 litres of water.

This is more interesting. He can fill the
5 litre bucket three times and pour
all the water into the tank

He can then drain 8 litres from the
tank into his 8 litre bucket. In this way
he is left with 7 litres of water in the tank.

1. Work out ways in which John can obtain the following quantities of water: (remember: no fractions!)
   (a) 3 litres; (b) 13 litres; (c) 2 litres; (d) 11 litres.

2. Work out ways in which he can obtain quantities of water from 1 litre all the way up to 25 litres.

3. Linda also has two buckets. One holds 7 litres and the other holds 9 litres.

Work out ways in which Linda can obtain quantities of water from 1 litre all the way up to 25 litres.

Part 4

4.1 NEGATIVE NUMBERS

Addition and subtraction

(a) $-7 + 2 = -5$
(b) $-6 - 5 = -11$
(c) $-3 + (-7) = -3 - 7 = -10$
(d) $-6 - (-10) = -6 + 10 = 4$

Exercise 1

Work out

1. $-6 + 2$
2. $-7 - 5$
3. $-3 - 8$
4. $-5 + 2$
5. $-6 + 1$
6. $8 - 4$
7. $4 - 9$
8. $11 - 19$
9. $4 + 15$
10. $-7 - 10$
11. $16 - 20$
12. $-7 + 2$
13. $-6 - 5$
14. $10 - 4$
15. $-4 + 0$
16. $-6 + 12$
17. $-7 + 7$
18. $2 - 20$
19. $8 - 11$
20. $-6 - 5$
21. $-3 + (-5)$
22. $-5 - (+2)$
23. $4 - (+3)$
24. $-3 - (-4)$
25. $6 - (-3)$
26. $16 + (-5)$
27. $-4 + (-4)$
28. $20 - (-22)$
29. $-6 - (-10)$
30. $95 + (-80)$
31. $-3 - (+4)$
32. $-5 - (+4)$
33. $6 + (-7)$
34. $-4 + (-3)$
35. $-7 - (-7)$
36. $3 - (-8)$
37. $-8 + (-6)$
38. $7 - (+7)$
39. $12 - (-5)$
40. $9 - (+6)$

Multiplication and division

(a) $-7 \times (-3) = 21$
(b) $-8 \times (+2) = -16$
(c) $-8 \div (-4) = 2$
(d) $10 \div (-2) = -5$

Exercise 2

Work out

1. $-3 \times (-2)$	2. $-8 \times (4)$
3. $2 \times (-3)$	4. $-6 \times (2)$
5. $-4 \times (4)$	6. $-3 \times (-3)$
7. $-6 \times (3)$	8. $4 \times (-10)$
9. $5 \times (-5)$	10. $8 \times (-100)$
11. $12 \div (-3)$	12. $16 \div (-1)$
13. $16 \div (-2)$	14. $-15 \div (-3)$
15. $-10 \div (-5)$	16. $-25 \div (5)$
17. $-8 \div (-2)$	18. $20 \div (-4)$
19. $-3 \times (+3)$	20. $-6 \times (0)$
21. $8 \div (-8)$	22. $-7 \div (-7)$
23. $40 \times (-10)$	24. $18 \times (-3)$
25. $100 \div (-1)$	26. $100 \div (-20)$
27. $-6 \times (-6)$	28. $-18 \div (-18)$
29. $0 \div (-7)$	30. $-25 \times (-20)$

Find two numbers

(a) Find two numbers whose *sum* is 12 and whose *product* is 20.
The numbers are 10 and 2.

(b) Find two numbers whose sum is 13 and whose product is 40.
The numbers are 8 and 5.

(c) Find two numbers whose sum is 2 and whose product is -15.
The numbers are -3 and 5.

(d) Find two numbers whose sum is -5 and whose product is 4.
The numbers are -1 and -4.

Exercise 3

1. Find two numbers whose sum is 5 and whose product is 6.
2. Find two numbers whose sum is 6 and whose product is 8.
3. Find two numbers whose sum is 7 and whose product is 12.
4. Find two numbers whose sum is 6 and whose product is 5.
5. Find two numbers whose sum is 8 and whose product is 12.

For questions **6** to **45** copy and complete the table.

	Sum	Product	Two numbers
6.	9	18	
7.	9	14	
8.	9	8	
9.	11	30	
10.	17	30	
11.	13	30	
12.	11	24	
13.	10	24	
14.	14	24	
15.	25	24	
16.	13	36	
17.	-3	2	
18.	-5	6	
19.	-6	8	
20.	-7	12	
21.	-7	10	
22.	-9	20	
23.	-10	24	
24.	-10	21	
25.	-13	42	
26.	-13	30	
27.	2	-3	
28.	-1	-6	
29.	1	-6	
30.	3	-4	
31.	-3	-4	
32.	-3	-10	
33.	-1	-12	
34.	5	-6	
35.	-2	-15	
36.	-2	-8	
37.	9	20	
38.	2	-8	
39.	-5	4	
40.	4	-12	
41.	-6	5	
42.	10	21	
43.	3	-10	
44.	-8	12	
45.	-9	8	

Questions on negative numbers are more difficult when the different sorts are mixed together. The remaining questions are given in the form of six short tests.

Test 1

1. $-8 - 8$
2. $-8 \times (-8)$
3. -5×3
4. $-5 + 3$
5. $8 - (-7)$
6. $20 - 2$
7. $-18 \div (-6)$
8. $4 + (-10)$
9. $-2 + 13$
10. $+8 \times (-6)$
11. $-9 + (+2)$
12. $-2 - (-11)$
13. $-6 \times (-1)$
14. $2 - 20$
15. $-14 - (-4)$
16. $-40 \div (-5)$
17. $5 - 11$
18. -3×10
19. $9 + (-5)$
20. $7 \div (-7)$

Test 2

1. $-2 \times (+8)$
2. $-2 + 8$
3. $-7 - 6$
4. $-7 \times (-6)$
5. $+36 \div (-9)$
6. $-8 - (-4)$
7. $-14 + 2$
8. $5 \times (-4)$
9. $11 + (-5)$
10. $11 - 11$
11. $-9 \times (-4)$
12. $-6 + (-4)$
13. $3 - 10$
14. $-20 \div (-2)$
15. $16 + (-10)$
16. $-4 - (+14)$
17. $-45 \div 5$
18. $18 - 3$
19. $-1 \times (-1)$
20. $-3 - (-3)$

Test 3

1. $-10 \times (-10)$
2. $-10 - 10$
3. $-8 \times (+1)$
4. $-8 + 1$
5. $5 + (-9)$
6. $15 - 5$
7. $-72 \div (-8)$
8. $-12 - (-2)$
9. $-1 + 8$
10. $-5 \times (-7)$
11. $-10 + (-10)$
12. $-6 \times (+4)$
13. $6 - 16$
14. $-42 \div (+6)$
15. $-13 + (-6)$
16. $-8 - (-7)$
17. $5 \times (-1)$
18. $2 - 15$
19. $21 + (-21)$
20. $-16 \div (-2)$

Test 4

1. $-4 + 4$
2. $-4 \times (+4)$
3. $-2 - 12$
4. $-2 \times (-12)$
5. $3 + (-4)$
6. $4 - (-10)$
7. $-22 \div 11$
8. $-9 + 7$
9. $-6 - (-13)$
10. $-3 \times (-11)$
11. $4 - 5$
12. $-20 - (+10)$
13. $4 \times (-7)$
14. $7 - (-12)$
15. $9 - 18$
16. $56 \div (-7)$
17. $7 - 6$
18. $-11 + (+2)$
19. $-2 \times (+8)$
20. $-8 \div (-2)$

Test 5

1. $-7 \times (-1)$
2. $-7 - 1$
3. $-11 + 2$
4. -11×2
5. $7 - (-4)$
6. $-3 + 16$
7. $-10 \div 5$
8. -6×3
9. $1 - 7$
10. $13 - (-2)$
11. $4 + (-7)$
12. $-9 - (-9)$
13. $-9 \times (-2)$
14. $-64 \div (-8)$
15. $16 - 14$
16. $-1 + (+7)$
17. $5 \div (-1)$
18. $-4 + (-4)$
19. $-4 \times (+10)$
20. $16 - 19$

Test 6

1. $-6 + 2$
2. $-6 \times (+2)$
3. $-10 \times (-5)$
4. $-10 - 5$
5. $-4 + (-5)$
6. $16 - 2$
7. $-14 \div (-2)$
8. $7 - (-4)$
9. $-2 + 20$
10. $-4 \times (-3)$
11. $17 + (-1)$
12. $7 \times (-2)$
13. $2 - 5$
14. $-8 - (-7)$
15. $-8 \div 8$
16. $-8 \times (-5)$
17. $6 - (-1)$
18. $-9 + (+14)$
19. $+81 \div (-9)$
20. $11 - 14$

4.2 ALGEBRAIC SUBSTITUTION

(a) A formula connecting velocities with acceleration and time is $v = u + at$. Find the value of v when $u = 3$
$$a = 4.$$
$$t = 6.$$
$$v = u + at$$
$$v = 3 + (4 \times 6)$$
$$v = 27$$

(b) A formula for the tension in a spring is $T = \dfrac{kx}{a}$.

Find the value of T when $k = 13$,
$$x = 5,$$
$$a = 2.$$
$$T = \frac{kx}{a}$$
$$T = \frac{13 \times 5}{2}$$
$$T = 32\tfrac{1}{2}$$

Exercise 4

1. A formula involving force, mass and acceleration is $F = ma$. Find the value of F when $m = 12$ and $a = 3$.

2. The height of a growing tree is given by the formula $h = 2t + 15$. Find the value of h when $t = 7$.

3. The time required to cook a joint of meat is given by the formula
$T =$ (mass of joint) $\times 3 + \tfrac{1}{2}$. Find the value of T when (mass of joint) $= 2\tfrac{1}{2}$.

4. An important formula in Physics states that
$I = mu - mv$.
Find the value of I when $m = 6$, $u = 8$, $v = 5$.

5. The distance travelled by an accelerating car is given by the formula $s = \left(\dfrac{u + v}{2}\right)t$. Find the value of s when $u = 17$, $v = 25$ and $t = 4$.

6. Einstein's famous formula states that $E = mc^2$. Find the value of E when $m = 5$ and $c = 20$.

7. The height of a stone thrown upwards is given by $h = ut - 5t^2$. Find the value of h when $u = 70$ and $t = 3$.

8. The speed of an accelerating particle is given by the formula $v^2 = u^2 + 2as$. Find the value of v when $u = 11$, $a = 5$ and $s = 6$.

9. If $m = 7x + 15$, find the values of m when
   (a) $x = 4$ (b) $x = 7$
   (c) $x = -2$ (d) $x = 10$.

10. If $T = 2x^2 - 12$, find the values of T when
    (a) $x = 3$ (b) $x = 2$
    (c) $x = 1$ (d) $x = 5$.

11. If $k = 3x^2 + x$, find the values of k when
    (a) $x = 2$ (b) $x = 4$
    (c) $x = -1$ (d) $x = 10$.

12. If $s = (2y)^2 - 6$, find the values of s when
    (a) $y = 2$ (b) $y = 3$
    (c) $y = -2$ (d) $y = 5$.

13. If $z = t^2 + yt$, find the values of z when
    (a) $t = 3$, $y = 4$ (b) $t = 7$, $y = 1$

14. If $p = (u - v)t$, find the values of p when
    (a) $u = 9$, $v = 2$, $t = 8$
    (b) $u = 11$, $v = \tfrac{1}{2}$, $t = 10$.

15. If $v = ut + \tfrac{1}{2}at^2$, find the values of v when
    (a) $u = 0$, $t = 6$, $a = 10$
    (b) $u = -2$, $t = 3$, $a = 10$.

Exercise 5

Work out, using $a = 3$, $b = 4$, $c = 5$, $d = 2$.

1. $a + b$	2. $c - b$
3. $3a + d$	4. $2b - a$
5. $4d - b$	6. $3c - d$
7. $a + 5b$	8. $c - 2d$
9. $3a + 2c$	10. $5a - 2b$
11. $ab + c$	12. $2ac$
13. $3cd$	14. $bc + cd$
15. $ad - c$	16. $bc - ad$
17. $3ab + c$	18. $5d + 2bc$
19. abc	20. $bcd + 10$
21. $cda - 6$	22. $3abd$
23. $acd + 4bd$	24. $abcd$
25. $bca - 20$	26. $17a - bcd$
27. $13a - cd$	28. $10acd + 3$
29. $10abcd$	30. $3ac - 5db$
31. $a^2 + 5$	32. $b^2 - 3$
33. $c^2 + d^2$	34. $a^2 + bc$
35. $d^3 - d$	36. $a^3 - b^2$
37. $c^2 - bc$	38. $d + d^3$
39. $d^4 - a^2$	40. $3a^2$

Exercise 6

Work out the values of the expressions in the exercise above using $a = 2$, $b = 1$, $c = 3$, $d = 4$.

Exercise 7

Work out, using $a = 3$, $b = -2$, $x = -1$, $y = 2$.

1. $a + b$
2. $b + y$
3. $a + x$
4. $y + x$
5. $a - y$
6. $a - b$
7. $y - x$
8. $b - y$
9. $x - a$
10. $y - b$
11. $a + b + x$
12. $b + y + x$
13. $a + b + x + y$
14. $2a + b$
15. $2y + x$
16. $3a - 4y$
17. $2b + y$
18. $3x + a$
19. $5a - b$
20. $x + 2b$
21. ab
22. by
23. xb
24. abx
25. bxy
26. $2ab$
27. $3bx$
28. $2xy + b$
29. $a + bx$
30. $y(a + b)$
31. $x(a + y)$
32. $b(a - x)$
33. $a(y - b)$
34. $2(ab + x)$
35. $5(xy + a)$
36. $a(bx + y)$
37. $a^2 + b^2$
38. $x^2 + y^2$
39. $2a^2$
40. $(2a)^2$
41. $3b^2$
42. $(3b)^2$
43. $5x^2$
44. $(5x)^2$
45. $(a + b)^2$
46. $(x + b)^2$
47. $(y + b)^3$
48. $(ax + y)^2$
49. $x^2(a - b)$
50. $b^2(a - x)$

Exercise 8

Work out the values of the expressions in the exercise above using $a = 2$, $b = -1$, $x = -3$, $y = 4$.

4.3   SOLVING EQUATIONS

Solve the equations
(a) $3x + 14 = 16$
$$3x = 16 - 14$$
$$3x = 2$$
$$x = \tfrac{2}{3}$$
(b) $4x - 5 = -2$
$$4x = -2 + 5$$
$$4x = 3$$
$$x = \tfrac{3}{4}$$
(c) $\qquad 7 = 2x + 15$
$$-15 + 7 = 2x$$
$$-8 = 2x$$
$$-4 = x$$

21. $9x - 4 = 1$
22. $11x - 10 = 1$
23. $15y + 2 = 5$
24. $7y + 8 = 10$
25. $4y - 11 = -8$
26. $3z - 8 = -6$
27. $4p + 25 = 30$
28. $5t - 6 = 0$
29. $9m - 13 = 1$
30. $4 + 3x = 5$
31. $7 + 2x = 8$
32. $5 + 20x = 7$
33. $3 + 8x = 0$
34. $50y - 7 = 2$

35. $200y - 51 = 49$
36. $5u - 13 = -10$
37. $9x - 7 = -11$
38. $11t + 1 = 1$
39. $3 + 8y = 40$
40. $12 + 7x = 2$
41. $6 = 3x - 1$
42. $8 = 4x + 5$
43. $9 = 2x + 7$
44. $11 = 5x - 7$
45. $0 = 3x - 1$
46. $40 = 11 + 14x$
47. $-4 = 5x + 1$
48. $-8 = 6x - 3$
49. $13 = 4x - 20$
50. $-103 = 2x + 7$

Exercise 9

Solve the equations.

1. $x - 7 = 5$
2. $x + 11 = 20$
3. $x + 12 = 30$
4. $x - 6 = -2$
5. $x - 8 = 9$
6. $x + 5 = 0$
7. $x - 13 = -7$
8. $x + 10 = 3$
9. $5 + x = 9$
10. $9 + x = 17$
11. $y - 6 = 11$
12. $y + 8 = 3$
13. $3x + 1 = 16$
14. $4x + 3 = 27$
15. $2x - 3 = 1$
16. $5x - 3 = 1$
17. $3x - 7 = 0$
18. $2x + 5 = 20$
19. $6x - 9 = 2$
20. $7x + 6 = 6$

Solve the equations
(a) $\quad 8x - 3 = 3x + 1$
$$8x - 3x = 1 + 3$$
$$5x = 4$$
$$x = \tfrac{4}{5}$$
(b) $\quad 3x + 9 = 18 - 7x$
$$3x + 7x = 18 - 9$$
$$10x = 9$$
$$x = \tfrac{9}{10}$$

Exercise 10

Solve the equations

1. $7x - 3 = 3x + 8$
2. $5x + 4 = 2x + 9$
3. $6x - 2 = x + 8$
4. $8x + 1 = 3x + 2$
5. $7x - 10 = 3x - 8$
6. $5x - 12 = 2x - 6$
7. $4x - 23 = x - 7$
8. $8x - 8 = 3x - 2$
9. $11x + 7 = 6x + 7$
10. $9x + 8 = 10$
11. $5 + 3x = x + 8$
12. $4 + 7x = x + 5$
13. $6x - 8 = 4 - 3x$
14. $5x + 1 = 7 - 2x$
15. $6x - 3 = 1 - x$
16. $3x - 10 = 2x - 3$
17. $5x + 1 = 6 - 3x$
18. $11x - 20 = 10x - 15$
19. $6 + 2x = 8 - 3x$
20. $7 + x = 9 - 5x$
21. $3y - 7 = y + 1$
22. $8y + 9 = 7y + 8$
23. $7y - 5 = 2y$
24. $3z - 1 = 5 - 4z$
25. $8 = 13 - 4x$
26. $10 = 12 - 2x$
27. $13 = 20 - 9x$
28. $8 = 5 - 2x$
29. $5 + x = 7 - 8x$
30. $3x + 11 = 2 - 3x$

16. $7(x - 3) = 10 - x$
17. $3(x + 1) = 2(x + 3) - 6$
18. $5(2x - 1) = 9(x + 1) - 8$
19. $3(x + 2) = 4(1 - x)$
20. $7(x + 3) = 2(3 - x)$
21. $3(2x + 1) = 4(5 - x)$
22. $5(x + 1) = 3(x - 2) + 12$
23. $3(x + 7) = 2(x + 1) + 20$
24. $2(2x - 1) = 3(1 - 2x)$
25. $5(3x + 1) = 2 + 3(x - 1)$
26. $3(x - 2) = 5 - 2(x + 2)$
27. $2(x + 1) = 7 - 3(x - 1)$
28. $3x - 1 = 8 - 2(2x + 1)$
29. $5(x - 2) = 6 - 3(x + 2)$
30. $7(2x + 1) = 5 - 4(2x - 3)$

Solve the equations
(a) $3(x - 1) = 2(x + 7)$
$3x - 3 = 2x + 14$
$3x - 2x = 14 + 3$
$x = 17$
(b) $5(2x + 1) = 3(x - 2) + 20$
$10x + 5 = 3x - 6 + 20$
$10x - 3x = -6 + 20 - 5$
$7x = 9$
$x = 1\frac{2}{7}$

Equations with fractions

Solve the equations (a) $\dfrac{7}{x} = 8$

(b) $\dfrac{3x}{4} = 2$

(a) $\dfrac{7}{x} = 8$

$7 = 8x$

$\dfrac{7}{8} = x$

(b) $\dfrac{3x}{4} = 2$

$3x = 8$

$x = \dfrac{8}{3}$

$x = 2\frac{2}{3}$

Exercise 11

Solve the equations

1. $2(x + 1) = x + 5$
2. $4(x - 2) = 2(x + 1)$
3. $5(x - 3) = 3(x + 2)$
4. $3(x + 2) = 2(x - 1)$
5. $5(x - 3) = 2(x - 7)$
6. $6(x + 2) = 2(x - 3)$
7. $10(x - 3) = x$
8. $3(2x - 1) = 4(x + 1)$
9. $4(2x + 1) = 5(x + 3)$
10. $3(x - 1) + 7 = 2(x + 1)$
11. $5(x + 1) + 3 = 3(x - 1)$
12. $7(x - 2) - 3 = 2(x + 2)$
13. $5(2x + 1) - 5 = 3(x + 1)$
14. $3(4x - 1) - 3 = x + 1$
15. $2(x - 10) = 4 - 3x$

Exercise 12

Solve the equations.

1. $\dfrac{3}{x} = 5$
2. $\dfrac{4}{x} = 7$
3. $\dfrac{11}{x} = 12$
4. $\dfrac{6}{x} = 11$
5. $\dfrac{2}{x} = 3$
6. $\dfrac{5}{y} = 9$
7. $\dfrac{7}{y} = 9$
8. $\dfrac{4}{t} = 3$
9. $\dfrac{3}{a} = 6$
10. $\dfrac{8}{x} = 12$
11. $\dfrac{3}{p} = 1$
12. $\dfrac{15}{q} = 10$
13. $5 = \dfrac{7}{t}$
14. $13 = \dfrac{4}{y}$
15. $3 = \dfrac{10}{x}$
16. $11 = \dfrac{4}{a}$
17. $-2 = \dfrac{3}{y}$
18. $-1 = \dfrac{5}{x}$
19. $-16 = \dfrac{7}{x}$
20. $-8 = \dfrac{4}{e}$
21. $\dfrac{10}{c} = -1$

22. $\dfrac{25}{m} = 5$ **23.** $\dfrac{4}{n} = 400$ **24.** $13 = \dfrac{2}{y}$

25. $\dfrac{5}{t} = 1$ **26.** $8 = \dfrac{15}{x}$ **27.** $-6 = \dfrac{3}{x}$

28. $\dfrac{x}{4} = 6$ **29.** $\dfrac{x}{5} = 3$ **30.** $\dfrac{y}{5} = -2$

31. $\dfrac{a}{7} = 3$ **32.** $\dfrac{t}{3} = 7$ **33.** $\dfrac{m}{4} = \dfrac{2}{3}$

34. $\dfrac{x}{7} = \dfrac{5}{8}$ **35.** $\dfrac{2x}{3} = 1$ **36.** $\dfrac{4x}{5} = 3$

37. $\dfrac{3y}{2} = 2$ **38.** $\dfrac{5t}{6} = 3$ **39.** $\dfrac{m}{8} = \dfrac{1}{4}$

40. $8 = \dfrac{5}{x}$ **41.** $19 = \dfrac{7}{y}$ **42.** $-5 = \dfrac{3}{a}$

43. $-6 = \dfrac{k}{4}$ **44.** $\dfrac{n}{7} = -10$ **45.** $4 = \dfrac{33}{q}$

46. $\dfrac{x}{2} = 110$ **47.** $\dfrac{500}{y} = -1$ **48.** $-99 = \dfrac{98}{f}$

Forming equations

The length of a rectangle is twice the width. If the perimeter is 36 cm, find the width.

(a) Let the width of the rectangle be x cm
Then the length of the rectangle is $2x$ cm

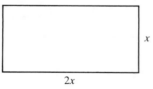

(b) Form an equation.
$x + 2x + x + 2x = 36$

(c) Solve $6x = 36$
$x = 6$
The width of the rectangle is 6 cm

Exercise 13

Solve each problem by forming an equation.

1. The length of a rectangle is three times the width. If the perimeter is 36 cm, find the width. (Let the width be x)

2. The length of a rectangle is five times the width. If the perimeter is 42 cm, find the width.

3. The length of a rectangle is 4 cm greater than its width. If the perimeter is 10 cm, find the width.

4. If the perimeter of the triangle is 29 units, find x.

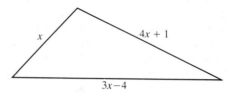

5. When a number is doubled and then added to 15, the result is 38. Find the number.

6. When a number is doubled and then added to 9, the result is 31. Find the number.

7. When a number is trebled and then added to 11, the result is 50. Find the number.

8. Find the area of the rectangle if the perimeter is 30 cm.

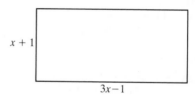

9. The length of a rectangle is 5 cm more than its width. If its perimter is 50 cm, what is its width?

10. If AB is a straight line, find x.

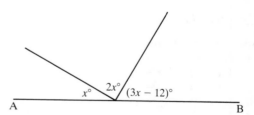

In questions **11** to **18** find the 'mystery' number.

11. If we subtract 3 from the number and then multiply the result by 2, the answer is 3.

12. If we add 9 to the number and then multiply the result by 7, the answer is 147.

13. If we subtract 11 from the number and then treble the result, the answer is 20.

14. If we double the number, add 4 and then multiply the result by 3, the answer is 13.

15. If we treble the number, take away 6 and then multiply the result by 2, the answer is 18.

16. If we double the number and subtract 7 we get the same answer as when we add 5 to the number.

17. If we multiply the number by 5 and subtract 4, we get the same answer as when we add 3 to the number and then double the result.

18. If we multiply the number by 6 and add 1, we get the same answer as when we add 5 to the number and then treble the result.

19. The sum of three consecutive whole numbers is 168. Find the numbers.

20. The sum of four consecutive whole numbers is 170. Find the numbers.

Simple inequalities

(a) Find the largest integer value of x if
   $3x < 10$

   $3x < 10$
   $x < 3\frac{1}{3}$
   $\therefore$ Largest integer value of x is 3.
   ['Integer' means whole number]

(b) Find the smallest integer value of x if
   $2x \geqslant 10$

   $2x \geqslant 10$
   $x \geqslant 5$
   $\therefore$ Smallest integer value of x is 5.

Exercise 14

In questions **1** to **16** find the largest integer value of x.

1. $2x < 11$
2. $3x < 8$
3. $4x < 21$
4. $10x < 30$
5. $3x \leqslant 12$
6. $2x \leqslant 9$
7. $3x \leqslant 10$
8. $5x < 7$
9. $3x < 50$
10. $2x \leqslant 50$
11. $9 > 2x$
12. $11 > 3x$
13. $16 \geqslant 4x$
14. $40 \geqslant 5x$
15. $1000 > 2x$
16. $100 > 3x$

In questions **17** to **30** find the smallest integer value of x.

17. $3x > 10$
18. $4x > 9$
19. $2x > 13$
20. $3x > 7$
21. $5x > 7$
22. $5x > 10$
23. $3x \geqslant 12$
24. $6x \geqslant 12$
25. $11 < 3x$
26. $801 < 10x$
27. $10 \leqslant 2x$
28. $24 \leqslant 4x$
29. $50 < 7x$
30. $4x > 100$

In questions **31** to **40** list all the integer values of x which satisfy the inequalities.

31. $x < 10\frac{1}{2}$ and $x > 8.1$
32. $2x < 12$ and $x > 3$
33. $3x < 14$ and $x > 0$
34. $5x \leqslant 20$ and $x > 1$
35. $3x \leqslant 30$ and $2x > 15$
36. $4x < 19$ and $3x > 5$
37. $2x \leqslant 20$ and $5x \geqslant 35$
38. $20 < 2x \leqslant 30$
39. $10 \leqslant 3x \leqslant 18$
40. $975 \leqslant 5x \leqslant 1000$

4.4   CHANGING THE SUBJECT OF A FORMULA

Make x the subject in the formulae below.

(a) $ax - p = t$
   $ax = t + p$
   $x = \dfrac{t + p}{a}$

(b) $y(x + y) = v^2$
   $yx + y^2 = v^2$
   $yx = v^2 - y^2$
   $x = \dfrac{v^2 - y^2}{y}$

Exercise 15

Make x the subject

1. $x + b = e$
2. $x - t = m$
3. $x - f = a + b$
4. $x + h = A + B$
5. $x + t = y + t$
6. $a + x = b$
7. $k + x = m$
8. $v + x = w + y$
9. $ax = b$
10. $hx = m$
11. $mx = a + b$
12. $kx = c - d$
13. $vx = e + n$
14. $3x = y + z$
15. $xp = r$
16. $xm = h - m$
17. $ax + t = a$
18. $mx - e = k$
19. $ux - h = m$
20. $ex + q = t$

21. $kx - u^2 = v^2$ **22.** $gx + t^2 = s^2$
23. $xa + k = m^2$ **24.** $xm - v = m$
25. $a + bx = c$ **26.** $t + sx = y$
27. $y + cx = z$ **28.** $a + hx = 2a$
29. $mx - b = b$ **30.** $kx + ab = cd$
31. $a(x - b) = c$ **32.** $c(x - d) = e$
33. $m(x + m) = n^2$ **34.** $k(x - a) = t$
35. $h(x - h) = k$ **36.** $m(x + b) = n$
37. $a(x - a) = a^2$ **38.** $c(a + x) = d$
39. $m(b + x) = e$ **40.** $n(x - n) = t^2$

21. $t = \dfrac{e}{x}$ **22.** $a = \dfrac{b}{x}$
23. $m = \dfrac{h}{x}$ **24.** $\dfrac{a}{b} = \dfrac{c}{x}$
25. $\dfrac{u}{x} = \dfrac{c}{d}$ **26.** $\dfrac{m}{x} = t^2$
27. $\dfrac{h}{x} = \sin 20°$ **28.** $\dfrac{e}{x} = \cos 40°$
29. $\dfrac{m}{x} = \tan 46°$ **30.** $\dfrac{a^2}{b^2} = \dfrac{c^2}{x}$

Formulae involving fractions

Make x the subject in the formulae below.

(a) $\dfrac{a}{x} = p$

$\quad x = ap$

(b) $\dfrac{m}{x} = t$

$\quad m = xt$

$\quad \dfrac{m}{t} = x$

Formulae with x^2 and negative x terms

Make x the subject of the formulae.

(a) $ax^2 = e$

$\quad x^2 = \dfrac{e}{a}$

$\quad x = \pm \sqrt{\left(\dfrac{e}{a}\right)}$

(b) $h - bx = m$

$\quad h = m + bx$

$\quad h - m = bx$

$\quad \dfrac{h - m}{b} = x$

Exercise 16

Make x the subject.

1. $\dfrac{x}{t} = m$ **2.** $\dfrac{x}{e} = n$

3. $\dfrac{x}{p} = a$ **4.** $am = \dfrac{x}{t}$

5. $bc = \dfrac{x}{a}$ **6.** $e = \dfrac{x}{y^2}$

7. $\dfrac{x}{a} = (b + c)$ **8.** $\dfrac{x}{t} = (c - d)$

9. $\dfrac{x}{m} = s + t$ **10.** $\dfrac{x}{k} = h + i$

11. $\dfrac{x}{b} = \dfrac{a}{c}$ **12.** $\dfrac{x}{m} = \dfrac{z}{y}$

13. $\dfrac{x}{h} = \dfrac{c}{d}$ **14.** $\dfrac{m}{n} = \dfrac{x}{e}$

15. $\dfrac{b}{e} = \dfrac{x}{h}$ **16.** $\dfrac{x}{(a + b)} = c$

17. $\dfrac{x}{(h + k)} = m$ **18.** $\dfrac{x}{u} = \dfrac{m}{y}$

19. $\dfrac{x}{(h - k)} = t$ **20.** $\dfrac{x}{(a + b)} = (z + t)$

Exercise 17

Make x the subject.

1. $cx^2 = h$ **2.** $bx^2 = f$
3. $x^2 t = m$ **4.** $x^2 y = (a + b)$
5. $mx^2 = (t + a)$ **6.** $x^2 - a = b$
7. $x^2 + c = t$ **8.** $x^2 + y = z$
9. $x^2 - a^2 = b^2$ **10.** $x^2 + t^2 = m^2$
11. $x^2 + n^2 = a^2$ **12.** $ax^2 = c$
13. $hx^2 = n$ **14.** $cx^2 = z + k$
15. $ax^2 + b = c$ **16.** $dx^2 - e = h$
17. $gx^2 - n = m$ **18.** $x^2 m + y = z$
19. $a + mx^2 = f$ **20.** $a^2 + x^2 = b^2$

21. $a - x = y$ **22.** $h - x = m$
23. $z - x = q$ **24.** $v = b - x$
25. $m = k - x$ **26.** $h - cx = d$
27. $y - mx = c$ **28.** $k - ex = h$
29. $a^2 - bx = d$ **30.** $m^2 - tx = n^2$
31. $v^2 - ax = w$ **32.** $y - x = y^2$
33. $k - t^2 x = m$ **34.** $e = b - cx$
35. $z = h - gx$ **36.** $a + b = c - dx$
37. $y^2 = v^2 - kx$ **38.** $h = d - fx$
39. $a(b - x) = c$ **40.** $h(m - x) = n$

The next two exercises are more difficult because they contain a wide variety of different formulae.

Exercise 18

Make the letter in brackets the subject.

1. $ax - d = h$ $[x]$
2. $zy + k = m$ $[y]$
3. $d(y + e) = f$ $[y]$
4. $m(a + k) = d$ $[k]$
5. $a + bm = c$ $[m]$
6. $ae^2 = b$ $[e]$
7. $yt^2 = z$ $[t]$
8. $x^2 - c = e$ $[x]$
9. $my - n = b$ $[y]$
10. $a(z + a) = b$ $[z]$
11. $\dfrac{a}{x} = d$ $[x]$
12. $\dfrac{k}{m} = t$ $[k]$
13. $\dfrac{u}{m} = n$ $[u]$
14. $\dfrac{y}{x} = d$ $[x]$
15. $\dfrac{a}{m} = t$ $[m]$
16. $\dfrac{d}{g} = n$ $[g]$
17. $\dfrac{t}{k} = (a + b)$ $[t]$
18. $y = \dfrac{v}{e}$ $[e]$
19. $c = \dfrac{m}{y}$ $[y]$
20. $\dfrac{a^2}{m} = b$ $[a]$
21. $g(m + a) = b$ $[m]$
22. $h(h + g) = x^2$ $[g]$
23. $y - t = z$ $[t]$
24. $me^2 = c$ $[e]$
25. $a(y + x) = t$ $[x]$
26. $uv - t^2 = y^2$ $[v]$
27. $k^2 + t = c$ $[k]$
28. $k - w = m$ $[w]$
29. $b - an = c$ $[n]$
30. $m(a + y) = c$ $[y]$
31. $pq - x = ab$ $[x]$
32. $a^2 - bk = t$ $[k]$
33. $v^2 z = w$ $[z]$
34. $c = t - u$ $[u]$
35. $xc + t = 2t$ $[c]$
36. $m(n + w) = k$ $[w]$
37. $v - mx = t$ $[m]$
38. $c = a(y + b)$ $[y]$
39. $m(a - c) = e$ $[c]$
40. $ba^2 = c$ $[a]$
41. $\dfrac{a}{p} = q$ $[p]$
42. $\dfrac{a}{n^2} = e$ $[n]$
43. $\dfrac{h}{f^2} = m$ $[f]$
44. $\dfrac{v}{x^2} = n$ $[x]$
45. $v - ac = t^3$ $[c]$
46. $a(a^2 + y) = b^3$ $[y]$
47. $ah^2 - d = b$ $[h]$
48. $h(h + k) = bc$ $[k]$
49. $u^2 - n^2 = v^2$ $[n]$
50. $m(b - z) = b^3$ $[z]$

Exercise 19

Make x the subject.

1. $a + x = p$
2. $y + x = m$
3. $z = k + x$
4. $u^2 = t^2 + x$
5. $a = bc + mx$
6. $z = k + ax$
7. $u^2 = e^2 + kx$
8. $m(a + x) = b$
9. $h = k(a + x)$
10. $y = p(p + x)$
11. $\dfrac{x}{k} = y$
12. $\dfrac{x}{m} = n$
13. $q = \dfrac{x}{q}$
14. $mn = \dfrac{x}{n}$
15. $\dfrac{m}{x} = a$
16. $e = \dfrac{n}{x}$
17. $w = \dfrac{u}{x}$
18. $\sin 32° = \dfrac{e}{x}$
19. $\frac{1}{2}zx = y$
20. $\frac{1}{3}kx = p$
21. $x^2 - n = m$
22. $v + x^2 = a - b$
23. $bx^2 - n = n^2$
24. $a(x - b) = d + e$
25. $k(x^2 - k) = mp$
26. $y - x = m$
27. $e(x - d) = u$
28. $a(y + x) = z$
29. $y(ex - f) = w$
30. $t(m + ax) = m$
31. $\dfrac{x}{(c + d)} = y$
32. $\dfrac{(a - b)}{x} = p$
33. $\dfrac{(m + n)}{x} = A$
34. $\dfrac{k}{x^2} = h$
35. $\dfrac{(A + B)}{x} = E$
36. $\frac{1}{4}kx = q$
37. $a(x^2 - d) = h$
38. $y = k^2 - x$
39. $g = m - nx$
40. $k = c(c - x)$

4.5 FACTORS

Factorise the following (a) $12a - 15b$
       (b) $3x^2 - 2x$
       (c) $2xy + 6y^2$

(a) $12a - 15b = 3(4a - 5b)$
(b) $3x^2 - 2x = x(3x - 2)$
(c) $2xy + 6y^2 = 2y(x + 3y)$

Exercise 20

In questions **1** to **10** copy and complete the statement.

1. $6x + 4y = 2(3x + \quad)$
2. $9x + 12y = 3(\quad + 4y)$
3. $10a + 4b = 2(5a + \quad)$
4. $4x + 12y = 4(\quad + \quad)$
5. $10a + 15b = 5(\quad + \quad)$
6. $18x - 24y = 6(3x - \quad)$
7. $8u - 28v = \quad(\quad - 7v)$
8. $15s + 25t = \quad(3s + \quad)$
9. $24m + 40n = \quad(3m - \quad)$
10. $27c - 72d = \quad(\quad - 8d)$

In questions **11** to **30** factorise the expression.

11. $20a + 8b$
12. $30x - 24y$
13. $27c - 33d$
14. $35u + 49v$
15. $12s - 32t$
16. $40x - 16t$
17. $24x + 84y$
18. $12x + 8y + 16z$
19. $12a - 6b + 9c$
20. $10x - 20y + 25z$
21. $20a - 12b - 28c$
22. $48m + 8n - 24x$

23. $42x + 49y - 21z$
24. $6x^2 + 15y^2$
25. $20x^2 - 15y^2$
26. $7a^2 + 28b^2$
27. $27a + 63b - 36c$
28. $12x^2 + 24xy + 18y^2$
29. $64p - 72q - 40r$
30. $36x - 60y + 96z$

Exercise 21

Factorise the following expressions.

1. $3x^2 + 2x$
2. $4x^2 - 3x$
3. $5x^2 + x$
4. $x^2 - 2x$
5. $2y^2 + 5y$
6. $4a^2 - 5a$
7. $6x^2 - 2x$
8. $12x^2 + 9x$
9. $10y^2 - 6y$
10. $7x^2 - 3x$
11. $10y^2 - 55y$
12. $12a^2 + 21a$
13. $x^3 + 2x^2 + 5x$
14. $2x^3 - 6x^2 + 2x$
15. $3x^3 + 3x^2 + 6x$
16. $2y^3 - 10y$
17. $12t^3 - 28t$
18. $u^3 + 2u^2 + 7u$
19. $4x^3 - 8x^2 - 4x$
20. $3ax + 2ay$

21. $4ax + 3bx$
22. $5cy + 2dy$
23. $4mx - 3my$
24. $an + 3bn$
25. $2ax - 10bx$
26. $6ax + 3ay$
27. $12ac + 16bc$
28. $6mx + 3my + 3mz$
29. $12px - 4py + 12pz$
30. $10x^3 - 5x^2 + 10x$
31. $6a^2m + 4am + 2m$
32. $6x^2y + 9xy + 12y$
33. $4wx - 5wy - 2wz$
34. $8at - 12bt + 14ct$
35. $16xy + 8y^2 + 24y$
36. $15ax + 20bx - 25x$
37. $36x^3 - 27x$
38. $45ax - 30bx + 60cx$
39. $84x^2y + 24y$
40. $18ux^2 + 27uy^2 + 45uz$

4.6 ROOTS AND INDICES

Squares and square roots

(a) $11^2 = 11 \times 11$
   $= 121$
(c) $\sqrt{36} = 6$

(b) $0.3^2 = 0.3 \times 0.3$
   $= 0.09$
(d) $\sqrt{0.01} = 0.1$

Exercise 22

Work out, without using a calculator.

1. 7^2
2. 3^2
3. 1^2
4. 10^2
5. 100^2
6. 9^2
7. 20^2
8. 0.1^2
9. 0.2^2
10. 8^2
11. 5^2
12. 4^2
13. 60^2
14. 12^2
15. $(\frac{1}{2})^2$
16. $\sqrt{4}$

17. $\sqrt{9}$ **18.** $\sqrt{100}$
19. $\sqrt{900}$ **20.** $\sqrt{121}$
21. $\sqrt{36}$ **22.** $\sqrt{10\,000}$
23. $\sqrt{1\,000\,000}$ **24.** $\sqrt{144}$
25. $\sqrt{1}$ **26.** $\sqrt{49}$
27. $\sqrt{0.01}$ **28.** $\sqrt{169}$
29. $\sqrt{\frac{1}{9}}$ **30.** $\sqrt{0}$
31. $(-1)^2$ **32.** $(-3)^2$
33. $(-5)^2$ **34.** $3^2 + (-3)^2$
35. $4^2 + (-4)^2$ **36.** $100^2 + \sqrt{100}$
37. $8^2 + \sqrt{9}$ **38.** $(-6)^2 - \sqrt{36}$
39. $1^2 - \sqrt{1}$ **40.** $5^2 - \sqrt{400}$
41. $(-6)^2 + (-2)^2$ **42.** $\sqrt{(3^2 + 4^2)}$
43. $\sqrt{(5^2 + 12^2)}$ **44.** $\sqrt{(6^2 + 8^2)}$
45. $\sqrt{(5^2 - 4^2)}$

Exercise 23

Use a calculator or square root tables to find the square root of the following numbers, correct to three significant figures.

1. 2	**2.** 5	**3.** 17
4. 6	**5.** 10	**6.** 101
7. 5.7	**8.** 8.21	**9.** 200
10. 427	**11.** 18.6	**12.** 0.94
13. 0.21	**14.** 12	**15.** 6072
16. 52 800	**17.** 428.8	**18.** 0.076
19. 0.095	**20.** 0.0074	**21.** 0.008 43
22. 1.1	**23.** 16	**24.** 2.36
25. 8060	**26.** 25 472	**27.** 61 616
28. 2 500 000	**29.** 0.8412	**30.** 72 000
31. 265	**32.** 1.756	**33.** 3.008
34. 19.62	**35.** 11.21	**36.** 0.074
37. 8.652	**38.** 61 111	**39.** 2333
40. 40 000	**41.** 36	**42.** 0.01
43. 7.841	**44.** 0.0085	**45.** 850 000
46. 7777	**47.** 232 323	**48.** 1007
49. 0.1555	**50.** 87.8	**51.** 2000
52. 47 600	**53.** 7	**54.** 1713

55. (a) 0.02   (b) 0.2   (c) 2
    (d) 20   (e) 200   (f) 2000
56. (a) 0.05   (b) 0.5   (c) 5
    (d) 50   (e) 500   (f) 5000
57. (a) 0.017   (b) 0.17   (c) 1.7
    (d) 17   (e) 170   (f) 1700
58. (a) 0.0006   (b) 0.006   (c) 0.06
    (d) 0.6   (e) 6   (f) 60

59. Describe the pattern you observe in questions **55** to **58**.

Cube roots by trial and error

Find the cube root of 17, correct to two significant figures, by trial and error.
(a) Try 2. $2^3 = 8$, too small.
(b) Try 3. $3^3 = 27$, too big.
(c) Try 2.5. $2.5^3 = 15.625$, too small.
(d) Try 2.6. $2.6^3 = 17.576$, too big.
(e) Try 2.55. $2.55^3 = 16.58$, too small.
(f) Try 2.58. $2.58^3 = 17.17$, too big.
(g) Try 2.57. $2.57^3 = 16.97$

Finally $\sqrt[3]{17} = 2.57$ correct to three significant figures.

Exercise 24

Find the cube root of the following numbers, using the method above. Give the answers correct to three significant figures.

1. 9	**2.** 11	**3.** 31
4. 60	**5.** 15	**6.** 100
7. 2	**8.** 300	**9.** 0.1
10. 0.01	**11.** 40 000	**12.** 800 000

Indices

Indices are used as a mathematical shorthand.

$2 \times 2 \times 2 \times 2 = 2^4$
$5 \times 5 \times 5 = 5^3$
$7 \times 7 \times 2 \times 2 \times 2 = 7^2 \times 2^3$
$3 \times 3 \times 3 \times 3 \times 10 \times 10 = 3^4 \times 10^2$

Exercise 25

Write in a form using indices.
1. $3 \times 3 \times 3 \times 3$
2. 5×5
3. $6 \times 6 \times 6$
4. $10 \times 10 \times 10 \times 10 \times 10$
5. $1 \times 1 \times 1 \times 1 \times 1 \times 1 \times 1$
6. $8 \times 8 \times 8 \times 8$
7. $7 \times 7 \times 7 \times 7 \times 7 \times 7$
8. $2 \times 2 \times 2 \times 5 \times 5$
9. $3 \times 3 \times 7 \times 7 \times 7 \times 7$
10. $3 \times 3 \times 10 \times 10 \times 10$
11. $5 \times 5 \times 5 \times 5 \times 11 \times 11$
12. $2 \times 3 \times 2 \times 3 \times 3$
13. $5 \times 3 \times 3 \times 5 \times 5$
14. $2 \times 2 \times 3 \times 3 \times 3 \times 3 \times 11 \times 11$

15. $7 \times 2 \times 3 \times 2 \times 7 \times 2 \times 3$
16. $5 \times 2 \times 2 \times 5 \times 5 \times 7 \times 2$
17. $3 \times 11 \times 3 \times 5 \times 3 \times 11 \times 3$
18. $6 \times 6 \times 5 \times 6 \times 5$
19. $2 \times 7 \times 2 \times 3 \times 2 \times 7 \times 3$
20. $5 \times 9 \times 5 \times 2 \times 7 \times 7 \times 9$
21. $a \times a \times a$
22. $c \times c \times c \times c$
23. $e \times e \times e \times e \times e$
24. $y \times y \times z \times z \times z$
25. $m \times m \times m \times n \times n$
26. $t \times t \times t \times t \times p \times p$
27. $u \times y \times y \times u \times u$
28. $m \times y \times m \times y \times y \times y$
29. $a \times e \times y \times e \times a \times e$
30. $n \times e \times e \times e \times e \times n \times n$

Exercise 26

Work out
1. 2^3 2. 3^2 3. 1^4
4. 3^3 5. 5^2 6. 2^2
7. 1^7 8. 10^2 9. 4^2
10. 4^3 11. 10^3 12. 2^5
13. 3^4 14. 5^3 15. 10^6
16. 7^2 17. $(-2)^2$ 18. $(-1)^2$
19. $(-1)^3$ 20. $(-2)^3$ 21. $(-3)^3$
22. $(-1)^5$ 23. $(-5)^2$ 24. $(-10)^3$
25. $(-4)^3$ 26. $(-2)^6$ 27. $(-1)^{10}$
28. $(-100)^2$ 29. 0.1^2 30. $(\frac{1}{2})^2$

Negative indices

$$2^{-3} = \frac{1}{2^3} = \frac{1}{8}$$

$$3^{-2} = \frac{1}{3^2} = \frac{1}{9}$$

$$x^{-5} = \frac{1}{x^5}$$

Exercise 27

In questions 1 to 12, work out the value of the number given.
1. 2^{-2} 2. 4^{-2} 3. 10^{-2}
4. 1^{-4} 5. 3^{-3} 6. 4^{-3}
7. 10^{-3} 8. 5^{-2} 9. 7^{-2}
10. 5^{-3} 11. 9^{-2} 12. 1^{-7}

In questions 13 to 42, answer 'true' or 'false'.
13. $2^3 = 8$ 14. $3^2 = 6$ 15. $5^3 = 125$
16. $2^{-1} = \frac{1}{2}$ 17. $10^{-2} = \frac{1}{20}$ 18. $3^{-3} = \frac{1}{9}$
19. $2^2 > 2^3$ 20. $2^3 < 3^2$ 21. $2^{-2} > 2^{-3}$
22. $3^{-2} < 3^3$ 23. $1^9 = 9$ 24. $(-3)^2 = -9$
25. $5^{-2} = \frac{1}{10}$ 26. $10^{-3} = \frac{1}{1000}$ 27. $10^{-2} > 10^{-3}$
28. $5^{-1} = 0.2$ 29. $10^{-1} = 0.1$ 30. $2^{-2} = 0.25$
31. $3^{-2} > 3^{-3}$ 32. $2^5 = 5^2$ 33. $2^4 = 4^2$
34. $(-2)^2 = 2^2$ 35. $(-2)^3 = 2^3$ 36. $10^{-2} = 0.01$
37. $1^{-10} = \frac{1}{10}$ 38. $3^4 < 4^3$ 39. $5^2 > 5^{-2}$
40. $2^{-3} > 1$ 41. $(-2)^3 > 1$ 42. $7^{-2} > 50^{-1}$

Multiplying and dividing

$$3^2 \times 3^4 = (3 \times 3) \times (3 \times 3 \times 3 \times 3) = 3^6$$
$$2^3 \times 2^2 = (2 \times 2 \times 2) \times (2 \times 2) = 2^5$$
$$7^3 \times 7^5 = 7^8 \text{ [add the indices]}.$$
$$2^4 \div 2^2 = \frac{2 \times 2 \times 2 \times 2}{2 \times 2} = 2^2$$
$$\left.\begin{array}{l} 5^6 \div 5^2 = 5^4 \\ 7^8 \div 7^3 = 7^5 \end{array}\right\} \text{ [subtract the indices]}.$$

Exercise 28

Write in a more simple form.
1. $5^2 \times 5^4$ 2. $6^3 \times 6^2$ 3. $10^4 \times 10^5$
4. $7^5 \times 7^3$ 5. $3^6 \times 3^4$ 6. $8^3 \times 8^3$
7. $2^3 \times 2^{10}$ 8. $3^6 \times 3^{-2}$ 9. $5^4 \times 5^{-1}$
10. $7^7 \times 7^{-3}$ 11. $5^{-3} \times 5^5$ 12. $3^{-2} \times 3^{-2}$
13. $6^{-3} \times 6^8$ 14. $5^{-2} \times 5^{-8}$ 15. $7^{-3} \times 7^9$

16. $7^4 \div 7^2$ 17. $6^7 \div 6^2$ 18. $8^5 \div 8^4$
19. $5^{10} \div 5^2$ 20. $10^7 \div 10^5$ 21. $9^6 \div 9^8$
22. $3^8 \div 3^{10}$ 23. $2^6 \div 2^2$ 24. $3^3 \div 3^5$
25. $7^2 \div 7^8$ 26. $3^{-2} \div 3^2$ 27. $5^{-3} \div 5^2$
28. $8^{-1} \div 8^4$ 29. $5^{-4} \div 5^1$ 30. $6^2 \div 6^{-2}$

31. $7^5 \times 7^3$ 32. $6^{-2} \times 6^6$ 33. $11^3 \times 11^{-5}$
34. $5^{-2} \div 5^3$ 35. $3^4 \div 3^{-1}$ 36. $7^5 \div 7^{-2}$
37. $3^{-4} \times 3^{10}$ 38. $10^{-3} \div 10^{-7}$ 39. $5^2 \times 5^{20}$
40. $\dfrac{2^3 \times 2^4}{2^2}$ 41. $\dfrac{3^4 \times 3^5}{3^3}$ 42. $\dfrac{5^4 \times 5^{-2}}{5^1}$
43. $\dfrac{7^7 \times 7^{-1}}{7^4}$ 44. $\dfrac{5^{-3} \times 5^{-2}}{5^2}$ 45. $\dfrac{2^5 \times 2^{-1}}{2^{-2}}$

Part 5

5.1 SPEED, DISTANCE AND TIME

Distance = Speed × Time.

$$\text{Speed} = \frac{\text{Distance}}{\text{Time}}.$$

$$\text{Time} = \frac{\text{Distance}}{\text{Speed}}.$$

1. A bird takes 20 s to fly a distance of 100 m. Calculate the average speed of the bird.

$\left(S = \dfrac{D}{T}\right)$ Average speed $= \dfrac{100}{20} = 5$ m/s.

2. A car travels a distance of 200 m at a speed of 25 m/s. How long does it take?

$$\left(T = \frac{D}{S}\right)$$

Time taken $= \dfrac{200}{25} = 8$ seconds

3. A boat sails at a speed of 12 knots for 2 days. How far does it travel?

1 knot = 1 nautical mile/hour
2 days = 48 hours

$(D = S \times T)$

Distance travelled $= 12 \times 48$
$\phantom{\text{Distance travelled }}= 576$ nautical miles

Exercise 1

The map shows several towns with the main roads joining them. The numbers indicate the distances in miles between each pair of towns.

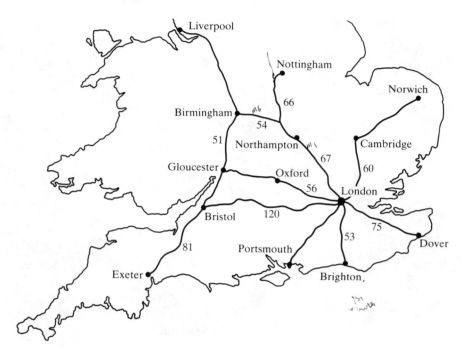

1. How far is it from Liverpool to Birmingham if the journey takes 2 hours at 49 mph?

2. How long does it take to travel from London to Cambridge at a speed of 30 mph?

3. What is the average speed of a car which travels from London to Bristol in three hours?

4. How far is it from Oxford to Gloucester if the journey takes seven hours at 7 mph?

5. An athlete runs from Exeter to Bristol at an average speed of 9 mph. How long does it take?

6. What is the average speed of a lorry which goes from Dover to London in $2\frac{1}{2}$ hours?

7. How far is it from Cambridge to Norwich if a man can walk the distance at a speed of 4 mph in $15\frac{1}{2}$ hours?

8. How long will a dog, running at 6 mph, take to run from Nottingham to Northampton?

9. A vintage car does the London to Brighton run in 20 hours. What is the average speed of the car?

10. A girl on a sponsored walk goes from Bristol to Gloucester in 11 hours at an average speed of 3.2 mph. How far is it from Bristol to Gloucester?

11. How long does it take a cyclist to travel from Birmingham to Northampton at a speed of 12 mph?

12. What is the average speed of a man on a horse who goes from London to Cambridge in 5 hours?

13. How far is it from London to Portsmouth if the journey takes 6 hours 15 minutes at a speed of 10 mph?

14. How long does it take to travel from Bristol to London at a speed of 80 mph?

15. A runaway horse runs from Brighton to London in 4 hours. What is the average speed of the horse?

Exercise 2

Copy and complete the table, giving correct units throughout.

	Speed	Distance	Time
1.	10 m/s	20 m	
2.		12 km	3 h
3.	12 mph	60 miles	
4.	100 cm/s		15 s
5.		15 km	2 h
6.	0.2 m/s		100 s
7.	11.4 km/h		4 h
8.	km/h	18 km	30 minutes
9.	18 feet/minute		10 minutes
10.		0.6 cm	10 s
11.	12 km/h	72 km	
12.	0.2 m/s		20 s
13.	5 cm/day	50 cm	
14.	0.05 m/s		10 s
15.	km/h	200 km	$\frac{1}{2}$ h
16.	0.02 km/year		100 years
17.	km/h	20 km	30 minutes
18.	100 m/s	1 m	
19.	26 cm/s	13 cm	
20.	5 m/day		15 days
21.	2 inches/s	60 inches	
22.	6 inches/s	3 feet	
23.	m/s	0.2 m	10 s
24.	250 mph	miles	15 minutes
25.	mph	18 miles	20 minutes

Exercise 3

1. If a car goes 15 miles in half an hour, how far does it go in one hour at the same speed?

2. If a lorry goes 18 km in 30 minutes, how far does it go in one hour at the same speed?

3. If a train travels 40 km in 20 minutes, how far does it go in one hour at the same speed?

4. A bird flies 8 miles in 15 minutes. How far will it fly in one hour?

5. A man runs at a speed of 9 mph. How far will he run in 20 minutes?

6. An aircraft flies at a speed of 600 mph. How far will it fly in 40 minutes?

7. A car runs at a speed of 40 mph. How far will it go in 1 hour 15 minutes?

8. A large whale swims at a speed of 15 km/h. How far will it swim in 40 minutes?

9. Find the time taken:
   (a) 8 miles at 16 mph
   (b) 20 km at 80 km/h
   (c) 12 miles at 16 mph
   (d) 50 m at 10 m/s.

10. Find the distance travelled:
    (a) 62 mph for 2 hours
    (b) 17 km/h for 4 hours
    (c) 84 mph for 30 minutes
    (d) 120 km/h for 15 minutes

11. Find the speed in km/h:
    (a) 17 km in 30 minutes
    (b) 22 km in 15 minutes
    (c) 15 km in 20 minutes
    (d) 23 km in 20 minutes

12. Find the distance travelled:
    (a) 19 mph for 30 minutes
    (b) 38 mph for 15 minutes
    (c) 36 km/h for 20 minutes
    (d) 80 km/h for 12 minutes

13. The distance from Manchester to Glasgow by road is 357 km. If a driver averages 70 km/h, find the time taken.

14. A car travels at an average speed of 45 mph. How long would a journey of 150 miles take in hours and minutes?

15. A British Rail High Speed Train goes from London to Newport at an average speed of 150 km/h and takes 1 hour 30 minutes over the journey.
    (a) State the time of arrival in Newport if it leaves London at 10 55.
    (b) Calculate the distance in kilometres between London and Newport.

16. In a car race the winning car passed the finishing line 5.5 seconds ahead of the car which came second. If both cars were travelling at 70 m/s, what was the distance between the two cars at the end?

17. Mr Steadman drove his car from Edinburgh to York. The record of his journey in both directions is given below. The distance from Edinburgh to York is 295 km.

Time

07 15   Left Edinburgh
09 15   Stopped for refreshment 160 km from Edinburgh
10 00   The journey to York continued
11 30   Arrived in York
15 00   Left York to travel back to Edinburgh.

(a) Calculate his average speed in km/h before he stopped for refreshment.
(b) Calculate the distance from York when he stopped for refreshment.
(c) Calculate his average speed for the second part of the journey.
(d) On the return journey from York to Edinburgh he averaged 59 km/h. Calculate the time of arrival in York.

5.2   PYTHAGORAS' THEOREM

Find x in the triangle shown.

2 cm

6 cm

$x^2 = 2^2 + 6^2$
$x^2 = 40$
$x = \sqrt{40}$
$x = 6.32$ cm (to 3 s.f.)

Exercise 4

Find the side marked with a letter. All lengths are in cm. Give answers correct to 3 s.f.

1.

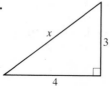
x
3
4

2.

x
6
5

3.

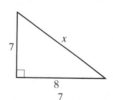
7
x
8

4.

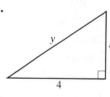
y
4
4

5.

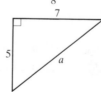
7
5
a

6.

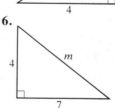
m
4
7

7.

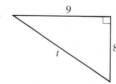
9
t
8

8.

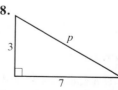
p
3
7

9.

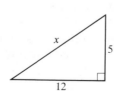
x
5
12

10.

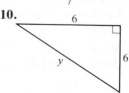
6
y
6

11.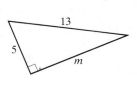

12.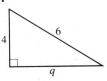

3.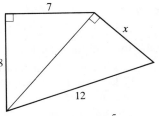

13.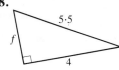

14.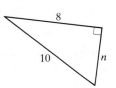

4.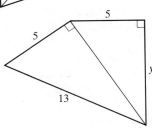

15.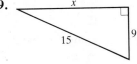

16.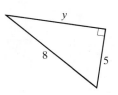

5.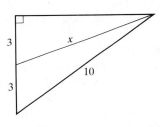

17.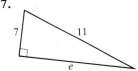

18.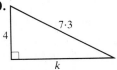

19. 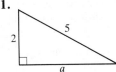   **20.**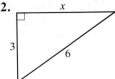

6.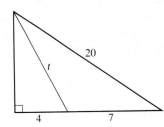

Exercise 5

Find the side marked with a letter. All lengths
are in cm. Give answers correct to 3 s.f.

1.

2.

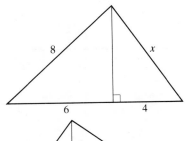

7.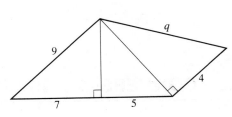

8.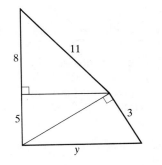

Exercise 6

Begin each question by drawing a clear diagram and let x be the length to be found.

1. A ship sails 9 km due North and then a further 17 km due East. How far is the ship from its starting point?

2. An aircraft flies 400 km due West and then a further 150 km due South. How far is the aircraft from its starting point?

3. A ladder of length 5 m leans against a vertical wall with its feet 2 m from the base of the wall. How high up the wall does the ladder reach?

4. A ship sails 7 km due North and then a further distance x km due West. The ship is then 12 km from its starting point. Calculate x.

5. A ladder of length 6 m leans against a vertical wall with its feet 3 m from the base of the wall. How high up the wall does the ladder reach?

6. A rectangle measures 8 cm by 5 cm. Calculate the length of the diagonals of the rectangle.

7. A rectangle of length 10 cm has diagonals of length 12 cm. Calculate the width of the rectangle.

8. A rectangle of width 6.5 cm has diagonals of length 10 cm. Calculate the length of the rectangle.

9. John is 20 m due North of Steven and Steven is 30 m due West of Peter. How far is John from Peter?

10. The diagram shows a rectangular block.

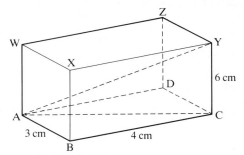

Calculate (a) AC   (b) AY

11. The diagram shows a rectangular block.

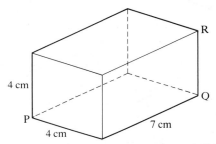

Calculate (a) PQ   (b) PR.

12. (a) Draw a diagram of a rectangular block 5 cm by 5 cm by 9 cm.
    (b) Calculate the length of the longest diagonal of the block.

5.3 CONVERSION GRAPHS

Exercise 7

Draw the graph and then answer the questions.

1. (a) Convert into dollars
      (i) £2   (ii) £1.60   (iii) £2.40
   (b) Convert into pounds
      (i) $1   (ii) $3.50   (iii) $2.50

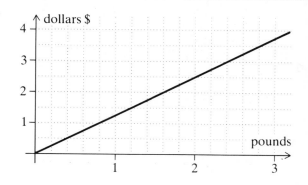

2. (a) Convert into German marks
  (i) £1   (ii) £3   (iii) £1.50
 (b) Convert into pounds
  (i) DM8   (ii) DM10   (iii) DM2
 (c) A book costs £2.50 in Britain. What is
      the equivalent cost in German money?

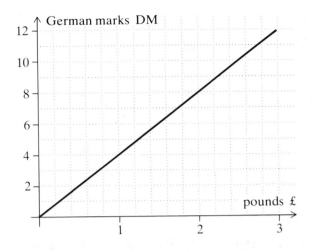

3. Give your answers as accurately as you can.
   [e.g. 3 lb = 1.4 kg approximately]

 (a) Convert into kilograms
  (i) 5.5 lb   (ii) 8 lb   (iii) 2 lb
 (b) Convert into pounds
  (i) 2 kg   (iii) 3 kg   (iii) 1.5 kg
 (c) A bag of sugar weighs 1 kg. What is its
      weight in pounds?
 (d) A washing machine has a weight limit of
      9 lb. What is the weight limit in
      kilograms?

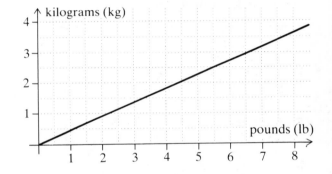

4. (a) Convert into litres
  (i) 2 gallons   (ii) 1.4 gallons
  (iii) 2.8 gallons
 (b) Convert into gallons
  (i) 10 litres   (ii) 7 litres
  (iii) 4 litres.
 (c) A drum contains 3 gallons of oil. How
      many litres of oil does it contain?
 (d) Car A consumes 2.4 gallons of fuel on a
      certain journey, while car B consumes
      11 litres of fuel. Which car consumes
      more fuel?

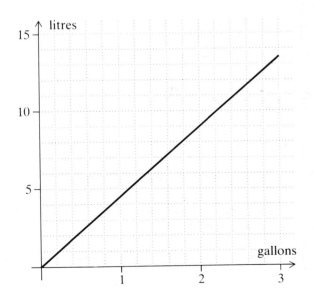

5. (a) Convert into km
   (i) 1 mile   (ii) 3 miles
   (iii) 2.2 miles
   (b) Convert into miles
   (i) 2 km   (ii) 5 km   (iii) 3.5 km
   (c) John can run 2 miles in 12 minutes while
       Steve can run 3 km in 12 minutes. Who
       is the faster runner?
   (d) Sarah lives 4.5 km from school and Jane
       lives 2.7 miles from school. Who lives
       nearer to school?

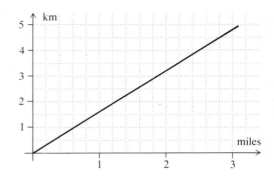

5.4 STRAIGHT LINE GRAPHS

The gradient of a line

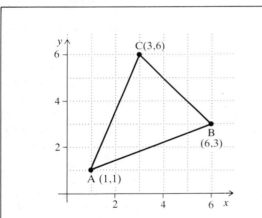

Gradient of line AB $= \dfrac{3-1}{6-1} = \dfrac{2}{5}$.

Gradient of line AC $= \dfrac{6-1}{3-1} = \dfrac{5}{2}$.

Gradient of line BC $= \dfrac{6-3}{3-6} = -1$.

A line which slopes upwards to the right
has a *positive* gradient.

A line which slopes upwards to the left has
a *negative* gradient.

Gradient $= \dfrac{\text{(difference in } y \text{ coordinates)}}{\text{(difference in } x \text{ coordinates)}}$

Exercise 8

1. Copy the diagram below.

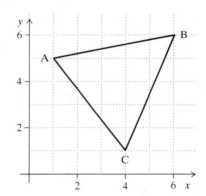

Find the gradients of AB, BC and AC.

2. Copy the diagram below.

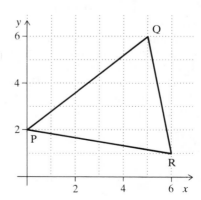

Find the gradients of PQ, PR and QR.

3. Copy the diagram below.

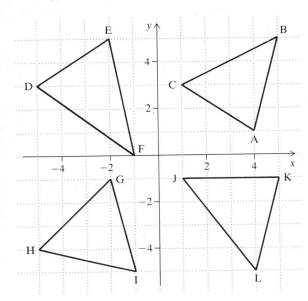

Find the gradients of the lines AB, BC, AC, DE, EF, DF, GH, HI, GI, JK, JL, KL.

4. Find the gradients of the lines joining the following pairs of points:
(a) $(3, 2) \rightarrow (4, 7)$
(b) $(-3, 4) \rightarrow (0, 6)$
(c) $(5, 1) \rightarrow (-2, 4)$
(d) $(-2, 8) \rightarrow (3, 0)$
(e) $(-1, 6) \rightarrow (-2, 7)$
(f) $(-3, -4) \rightarrow (8, -1)$
(g) $(6, 2) \rightarrow (8, 2)$
(h) $(-3, 4) \rightarrow (-2, -6)$
(i) $(0, 7) \rightarrow (-8, 7)$
(j) $(3, 2) \rightarrow (4, -2)$
(k) $(6, 5) \rightarrow (6, 3)$
(l) $(3, -8) \rightarrow (3, 11)$

5. The diagram shows the graph of $y = \dfrac{10}{x}$.

A tangent to the curve has been drawn at the point $(2, 5)$.

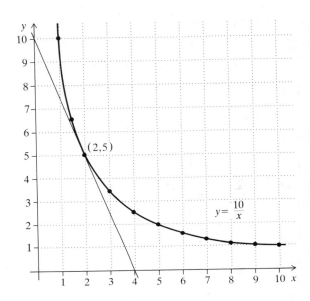

(a) Draw your own graph of $y = \dfrac{10}{x}$ and draw a tangent to the curve at $(2, 5)$
(b) Find the gradient of the tangent.
(c) Draw a tangent to the curve at $(4, 2.5)$. What is the gradient of the tangent?

6. (a) Draw the graph of $y = x^2$ for values of x from 0 to 5. Use a scale of 2 cm to 1 unit for x and 1 cm to 2 units for y.
(b) Draw a tangent to the curve at $(1, 1)$ and find the gradient of the tangent.
(c) Draw a tangent to the curve at $(3, 9)$ and find the gradient of the tangent.

5.5 PLOTTING GRAPHS

Draw the graph of $y = x^2 - 3x - 2$ for values of x from -2 to 4.

x	-2	-1	0	1	2	3	4
x^2	4	1	0	1	4	9	16
$-3x$	6	3	0	-3	-6	-9	-12
-2	-2	-2	-2	-2	-2	-2	-2
y	8	2	-2	-4	-4	-2	2

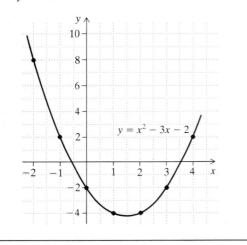

Exercise 9

In each question make a table of values and then draw the graph. Suggested scales: 1 cm to 1 unit on both axes, unless otherwise stated.

1. $y = 2x - 1$; x from -3 to $+3$

x	-3	-2	-1	0	1	2	3
$2x$	-6	-4					
-1	-1	-1	-1				
y	-7	-5					

2. $y = 3x + 1$; x from -2 to $+3$.
3. $y = x - 3$; x from -4 to $+3$.
4. $y = 2x - 7$; x from -2 to $+5$.
5. $y = 4x + 2$; x from -3 to $+3$.
  [Use scales of 1 cm to 1 unit for x and 1 cm to 2 units for y].
6. $y = 5x - 3$; x from -2 to $+2$.
  [Scales as in question **5**].

7. $y = 8 - 2x$; x from -2 to $+4$

x	-2	-1	0	1	2	3	4
8	8	8	8				
$-2x$	4	2					
y	12	10					

8. $y = 6 - x$; x from -3 to $+3$.
9. $y = 10 - 3x$; x from -2 to $+3$.

For questions **10** to **16**, use scales of 2 cm to 1 unit for x and 1 cm to 1 unit for y.

10. $y = x^2 + 3x$; x from -4 to $+2$
11. $y = x^2 + 4x$; x from -4 to $+1$.
12. $y = x^2 - 2x$; x from -3 to $+3$.
13. $y = x^2 - 3x + 5$; x from -2 to $+4$.
14. $y = x^2 + 2x - 7$; x from -3 to $+3$.
15. $y = x^2 - 4x + 3$; x from -2 to $+4$.
16. $y = 2x^2 + 3x - 1$; x from -3 to $+2$.

For questions **17** to **20**, use a scale of 1 cm to 1 unit for both axes.

17. $y = \dfrac{8}{x}$; x from 1 to 8.

18. $y = \dfrac{12}{x}$; x from 1 to 12.

19. $y = \dfrac{4}{x}$; x from -4 to 4.

20. $y = \dfrac{10}{x}$; x from -5 to 5.

Graphical solution of equations

Draw the graphs of $y = x^2 - 2x$ and
$y = x + 1$. Hence find approximate
solutions to the equation
$x^2 - 2x = x + 1$.

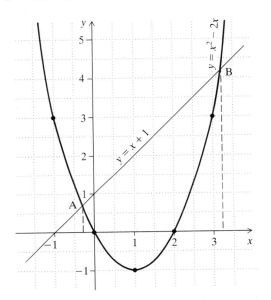

The solutions to the equation are given by
the x values at the two points of
intersection.

At A $x \approx -0.3$ ⎫ These are the
At B $x \approx$ 3.3 ⎬ approximate solutions

Exercise 10

1. (a) Draw axes with x from -4 to $+6$ and y
       from -7 to $+7$. Use a scale of 1 cm to
       1 unit for both axes.
   (b) Draw the graphs of the following:
       $y = 2x$; $y = x + 3$; $y = x - 2$; $y = 3$;
       $y = 6 - x$.
   (c) Use the graphs to solve the equations
       (i) $x - 2 = 6 - x$
       (ii) $x + 3 = 2x$,
       (iii) $2x = x - 2$,
       (iv) $x + 3 = 6 - x$,
       (v) $2x = 6 - x$,
       (vi) $6 - x = 3$.

2. (a) Draw axes with x from 0 to 8 and y from
       -4 to 8. Use a scale of 1 cm to 1 unit
       for both axes.
   (b) Draw the graphs of the following:
       $y = x - =4$; $y = 3$; $y = 0$; $y = 3 - x$;
       $y = 8 - 2x$.
   (c) Hence solve the equations
       (i) $x - 4 = 3$,
       (ii) $3 - x = 3$,
       (iii) $8 - 2x = x - 4$,
       (iv) $3 - x = 8 - 2x$,
       (v) $x - 4 = 3 - x$,
       (vi) $8 - 2x = 3$
       (vii) $3 - x = 0$,
       (viii) $8 - 2x = 0$.

3. (a) Draw axes with x from -4 to 8 and y
       from -4 to 8. Use a scale of 1 cm to
       1 unit for both axes.
   (b) Draw the graphs of the following:
       $y = 2x - 7$; $y = x$; $y = 5 - x$;
       $y = 2 - x$; $y = -3$.
   (c) Hence solve the equations:
       (i) $2x - 7 = x$,
       (ii) $2x - 7 = -3$,
       (iii) $5 - x = x$
       (iv) $5 - x = 2x - 7$,
       (v) $2 - x = x$,
       (vi) $5 - x = -3$,
       (vii) $2 - x = -3$.

4. (a) Draw axes with x from -6 to 4 and y
       from -20 to 10. Use a scale of 1 cm to
       1 unit for x and 2 cm to 5 units for y.
   (b) Draw the graphs of the following:
       $y = x^2 + 2x - 15$; $y = x$; $y = -5$;
       $y = 0$; $y = -19$.
   (c) Hence solve the equations:
       (i) $x^2 + 2x - 15 = -5$
       (ii) $x^2 + 2x - 15 = 0$
       (iii) $x^2 + 2x - 15 = -19$
       (iv) $x^2 + 2x - 15 = x$

5. (a) Draw axes with x from -4 to 4 and y from -6 to 8. Use a scale of 1 cm to 1 unit for both axes.
   (b) Draw the graphs of the following:
   $y = x^2 - 6$; $y = 4 - x$; $y = -3$; $y = 4$; $y = 0$; $y = x$.
   (c) Hence solve the equations:
      (i) $x^2 - 6 = 4$
      (ii) $x^2 - 6 = 0$
      (iii) $x^2 - 6 = -3$
      (iv) $x^2 - 6 = x$
      (v) $x^2 - 6 = 4 - x$

6. (a) Draw axes with x from -8 to 8 and y from -8 to 8. Use a scale of 1 cm to 1 unit for both axes.
   (b) Draw the graphs of the following:
   $y = 8 - x$; $y = \dfrac{8}{x}$; $y = x$; $y = 2x$; $y = 6$.
   (c) Hence solve the equations:

   (i) $\dfrac{8}{x} = 6$ (ii) $\dfrac{8}{x} = x$

   (iii) $\dfrac{8}{x} = 2x$ (iv) $\dfrac{8}{x} = 8 - x$

7. (a) Draw axes with x from -4 to 4 and y from -4 to 4. Use a scale of 2 cm to 1 unit for both axes.
   (b) Draw the graphs of the following:
   $y = \dfrac{4}{x}$; $y = \dfrac{x}{2}$; $y = x - 2$; $y = -3.5$.
   (c) Hence solve the equations:

   (i) $\dfrac{4}{x} = -3.5$,   (ii) $\dfrac{4}{x} = x - 2$,

   (iii) $\dfrac{4}{x} = \dfrac{x}{2}$.

8. (a) Draw axes with x from -4 to 4 and y from 0 to 16. Use a scale of 2 cm to 1 unit for x and 1 cm to 1 unit for y.
   (b) Draw the graphs of the following:
   $y = x^2$; $y = x + 10$; $y = 2x + 3$; $y = x + 5$; $y = 7 - x$.
   (c) Hence solve the equations:
      (i) $x^2 - x - 5 = 0$
      (ii) $x^2 - x - 10 = 0$
      (iii) $x^2 - 2x - 3 = 0$
      (iv) $x^2 - 7 + x = 0$

Graphical solution of simultaneous equations

Solve the simultaneous equations
$$2x + 3y = 12 \qquad \ldots [A]$$
$$2x + y = 8 \qquad \ldots [B]$$
Draw lines [A] and [B] and find where they meet.

Quick method:
  For line [A] $2x + 3y = 12$
  when $x = 0, y = 4$
                 $y = 0, x = 6$
Draw line [A] through these two points.
  For line [B] $2x + y = 8$
        when $x = 0, y = 8$
               $y = 0, x = 4$

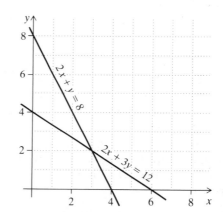

The lines meet at the point $(3, 2)$ so the solutions are $x = 3$, $y = 2$.

Exercise 16

Solve the simultaneous equations by drawing graphs.

1. $x + y = 6$
   $2x + y = 8$
   Draw axes with x and y from 0 to 8.

2. $x + 2y = 8$
   $3x + y = 9$
   Draw axes with x and y from 0 to 9.

3. $x + 2y = 11$
   $2x + y = 13$
   Draw axes with x and y from 0 to 13.

4. $2x + 3y = 12$
   $x + y = 5$
   Draw axes with x and y from 0 to 7.

5. $3x + 4y = 24$
   $3x + 2y = 18$
   Draw axes with x and y from 0 to 9.

6. $x + 3y = 6$
   $x - y = 2$
   Draw axes with x from 0 to 8 and y from -2 to 4.

7. $5x + y = 10$
   $x - y = -4$
   Draw axes with x from -4 to 4 and y from 0 to 10.

Exercise 17

The graphs in this exercise are much more difficult and are intended for enthusiasts only! Draw the graphs using the axes indicated.

1. $y = 6 + 2x - x^2$; x from -3 to 4.
   Scales: x 2 cm = 1 unit;
      y 2 cm = 5 units.

2. $y = 15 - 2x - x^2$; x from -3 to 4.
   Scales: x 2 cm = 1 unit;
      y 2 cm = 5 units.

3. $y = 3x^2$; x from -3 to 3.
   Scales: x 2 cm = 1 unit;
      y 2 cm = 5 units.

4. $y = 2x^2 + 4x - 11$; x from -3 to 3.
   Scales: x 2 cm = 1 unit;
      y 2 cm = 5 units.

5. $y = \dfrac{8}{x^2}$; $x = \pm 1, \pm 2; \pm 3, \pm 4$.
   Scales: x 2 cm = 1 unit;
      y 1 cm = 1 unit.

6. $y = 2x + \dfrac{8}{x}$; $x = \pm\frac{1}{2}, \pm 1, \pm 2, \pm 3, \pm 4, \pm 5, \pm 6$.
   Scales: x 1 cm = 1 unit;
      y 2 cm = 5 units.

7. $y = x^2 + \dfrac{10}{x}$; $x = \pm\frac{1}{2}, \pm 1, \pm 2, \pm 3, \pm 4$.
   Scales: x 2 cm = 1 unit;
      y 2 cm = 5 units.

8. $y = x^3 - 16x$; x from -5 to 5.
   Scales: x 1 cm = 1 unit;
      y 10 cm = 1 unit.

9. $y = \dfrac{4}{x^2} + x^2$; $x = \pm\frac{1}{2}, \pm 1, \pm 1\frac{1}{2}, \pm 2, \pm 3, \pm 4$.
   Scales: x 2 cm = 1 unit;
      y 5 cm = 2 units.

10. $y = \dfrac{4}{x^2} - x^2$; $x = \pm\frac{1}{2}, \pm 1, \pm 2, \pm 3, \pm 4$.
   Scales: x 2 cm = 1 unit;
      y 5 cm = 2 units.

11. $y = x^2 + 2x + \dfrac{4}{x}$;
   $x = \pm\frac{1}{4}, \pm\frac{1}{2}, \pm 1, \pm 2, \pm 3, \pm 4$.
   Scales: x 2 cm = 1 unit;
      y 5 cm = 2 units.

12. $y = 2^x$; $x = -4$ to 4.
   Scales: x 2 cm = 1 unit;
      y 1 cm = 1 unit.

Part 6

6.1 TRANSFORMATIONS

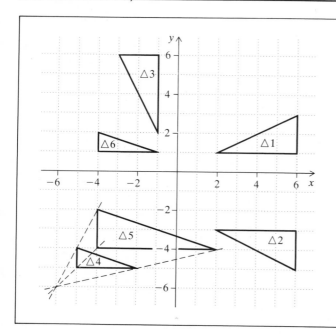

(a) Reminder

$\triangle 1 \to \triangle 2$: reflection in the line $y = -1$.

$\triangle 1 \to \triangle 3$: rotation 90° anticlockwise, centre (0, 0).

$\triangle 4 \to \triangle 5$: enlargement, scale factor 2, centre $(-6, -6)$.

$\triangle 4 \to \triangle 6$: translation $\begin{pmatrix} 1 \\ 6 \end{pmatrix}$

(b) Congruence

$\triangle 1$, $\triangle 2$ and $\triangle 3$ are congruent.

$\triangle 4$ and $\triangle 6$ are congruent.

$\triangle 5$ is not congruent to any other triangle.

Describing transformations

Exercise 1

In this exercise you are given an object triangle
and its image after various unknown
transformations. Your task is to describe the
transformation which maps the object onto the
image. Questions **1** to **6** involve rotations,
reflections and translations. Questions **7** and **8**
involve enlargements as well.

1. Copy the diagram below.

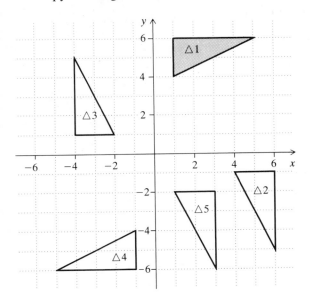

Describe fully the following rotations:
(a) △1 → △2   (b) △1 → △3
(c) △1 → △4   (d) △1 → △5.
[Give the angle, the direction and the
centre].

In questions **2** and **3**, draw axes with x and y
from −8 to +8.

2. Plot and label the following triangles:
△1: (8, 1), (8, 5), (6, 5)
△2: (1, −8), (5, −8), (5, −6)
△3: (−4, 7), (−4, 3), (−2, 3)
△4: (2, −3), (6, −1), (6, −3)
△5: (−4, −3), (−4, −7), (−2, −7)

Describe fully the following rotations;
(a) △1 → △2   (b) △1 → △3
(c) △1 → △4   (d) △1 → △5
(e) △4 → △5   (f) △3 → △4
(g) △2 → △1

3. Plot and label the following triangles:
△1: (−4, 3), (−4, 5), (0, 5)
△2: (3, 8), (5, 8), (5, 4)
△3: (−4, −7), (0, −5), (0, −7)
△4: (3, −2), (5, −2), (5, −6)
△5: (−5, −4), (−7, −4), (−7, 0)

Describe fully the following rotations:
(a) △1 → △2   (b) △1 → △3
(c) △1 → △4   (d) △1 → △5
(e) △5 → △3   (f) △3 → △4
(g) △5 → △2   (h) △4 → △1

4. Copy the diagram below

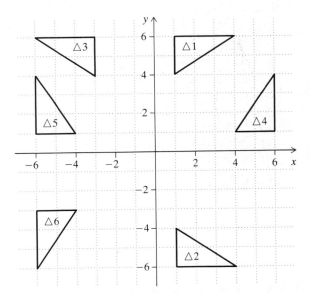

Describe fully the following reflections:
(a) △1 → △2   (b) △1 → △3
(c) △1 → △4   (d) △4 → △5
(e) △5 → △6   (f) △2 → △5

In questions **5** to **8**, draw axes with x and y from
−8 to +8.

5. Plot and label the following triangles
△1: (−6, 6), (−2, 6), (−2, 4)
△2: (2, 4), (4, 4), (4, 8)
△3: (4, 3), (8, 3), (8, 1)
△4: (4, −2), (6, −2), (6, −6)
△5: (−2, −4), (−2, −6), (−6, −6)

Describe fully the following transformations
(a) △1 → △2   (b) △1 → △3
(c) △1 → △4   (d) △1 → △5
(e) △2 → △3   (f) △4 → △5

6. Plot and label the following triangles
△1: (2, 6), (2, 8), (6, 8)
△2: (2, −4), (2, −6), (6, −6)
△3: (−6, −2), (−4, −2), (−6, −6)
△4: (4, −2), (6, −2), (6, −6)
△5: (−2, 6), (−2, 4), (2, 4)
△6: (−6, −6), (−2, −4), (−2, −6)

Describe fully the following transformations
(a) △1 → △2   (b) △2 → △4
(c) △2 → △3   (d) △2 → △5
(e) △3 → △5   (f) △3 → △6
(g) △1 → △6   (h) △3 → △4

7. Plot and label the following triangles
△1: (−5, −5), (−1, −5), (−1, −3)
△2: (1, 7), (1, 3), (3, 3)
△3: (3, −3), (7, −3), (7, −1)
△4: (−5, −5), (−5, −1), (−3, −1)
△5: (1, −6) (3, −6), (3, −5)
△6: (−3, 3), (−3, 7), (−5, 7)

Describe fully the following transformations
(a) △1 → △2   (b) △1 → △3
(c) △1 → △4   (d) △1 → △5
(e) △1 → △6   (f) △5 → △3
(g) △2 → △3

Which triangles are congruent to △1?

8. Plot and label the following triangles
△1: (−3, −6), (−3, −2), (−5, −2)
△2: (−5, −1), (−5, −7), (−8, −1)
△3: (−2, −1), (2, −1), (2, 1)
△4: (6, 3), (2, 3), (2, 5)
△5: (8, 4), (8, 8), (6, 8)
△6: (−3, 1), (−3, 3) (−4, 3)

Describe fully the following transformations:
(a) △1 → △2   (b) △1 → △3
(c) △1 → △4   (d) △1 → △5
(e) △1 → △6   (f) △3 → △5
(g) △6 → △2

Which triangles are congruent to △1?

Successive transformations

Exercise 2

This exercise contains questions involving a combination of successive reflections, rotations and translations.

1. (a) Copy the diagram on the right.
   (b) Draw the triangles △2, △3, △5 and △6 as follows:
      (i)   △1 → △2: reflection in *y*-axis.
      (ii) △2 → △3: rotation 90° anticlockwise, centre (0, 0).
      (iii) △4 → △5: reflection in *y*-axis.
      (iv) △5 → △6: rotation 90° anticlockwise, centre (2, −2).
   (c) Write down the coordinates of the 'pointed ends' of triangles △2, △3, △5 and △6.

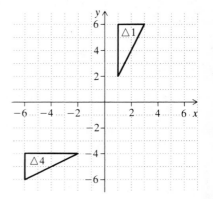

For questions **2** to **5**, draw a pair of axes with values of x and y from -8 to $+8$.

2. (a) Plot and label
    $\triangle 1$: (1, 6), (1, 8), (5, 8).
    $\triangle 4$: $(-2, -8)$, $(-7, -8)$, $(-7, -5)$.
   (b) Draw the triangles $\triangle 2$, $\triangle 3$, $\triangle 5$ and $\triangle 6$ as follows:
      (i) $\triangle 1 \rightarrow \triangle 2$: reflection in the line $y = x$.
      (ii) $\triangle 2 \rightarrow \triangle 3$: reflection in the x-axis.
      (iii) $\triangle 4 \rightarrow \triangle 5$: rotation 90° clockwise, centre (0, 0).

      (iv) $\triangle 5 \rightarrow \triangle 6$: translation $\begin{pmatrix} 5 \\ -2 \end{pmatrix}$.
   (c) Write down the coordinates of the 'pointed ends' of triangles $\triangle 2$, $\triangle 3$, $\triangle 5$ and $\triangle 6$.

3. (a) Plot and label
    $\triangle 1$: $(-4, 4)$, $(-4, 6)$, $(-8, 6)$.
    $\triangle 4$: $(-8, -2)$, $(-8, -6)$, $(-6, -6)$.
   (b) Draw the triangles $\triangle 2$, $\triangle 3$, $\triangle 5$ and $\triangle 6$ as follows:
      (i) $\triangle 1 \rightarrow \triangle 2$: rotation 90° clockwise, centre (0, 0).
      (ii) $\triangle 2 \rightarrow \triangle 3$: reflection in the line $y = 3$.
      (iii) $\triangle 4 \rightarrow \triangle 5$: reflection in the line $y = x$.
      (iv) $\triangle 5 \rightarrow \triangle 6$: rotation 180°, centre $(-2, -5)$.
   (c) Write down the coordinates of the 'pointed ends' of triangles $\triangle 2$, $\triangle 3$, $\triangle 5$ and $\triangle 6$.

4. (a) Plot and label
    $\triangle 1$: $(-3, 4)$, $(-3, 8)$, $(-1, 8)$
    $\triangle 5$: $(-8, -2)$, $(-8, -6)$, $(-6, -2)$
   (b) Draw the triangles $\triangle 2$, $\triangle 3$, $\triangle 4$, $\triangle 6$ and $\triangle 7$ as follows:

      (i) $\triangle 1 \rightarrow \triangle 2$: translation $\begin{pmatrix} 9 \\ -4 \end{pmatrix}$.   (ii) $\triangle 2 \rightarrow \triangle 3$: translation $\begin{pmatrix} -4 \\ -8 \end{pmatrix}$.

      (iii) $\triangle 3 \rightarrow \triangle 4$: reflection in the line $y = x$.
      (iv) $\triangle 5 \rightarrow \triangle 6$: rotation 90° anticlockwise, centre $(-4, -1)$.
      (v) $\triangle 6 \rightarrow \triangle 7$: rotation 180°, centre $(0, -1)$.
   (c) Write down the coordinates of the 'pointed ends' of triangles $\triangle 2$, $\triangle 3$, $\triangle 4$, $\triangle 6$ and $\triangle 7$.

5. (a) Plot and label
    $\triangle 1$: $(8, -3)$, $(3, -3)$, $(3, -6)$.
   (b) Draw the triangles $\triangle 2$, $\triangle 3$, $\triangle 4$, $\triangle 5$ and $\triangle 6$ as follows:
      (i) $\triangle 1 \rightarrow \triangle 2$: rotation 90° anticlockwise, centre (1, 1).
      (ii) $\triangle 2 \rightarrow \triangle 3$: reflection the line $x = 2$.
      (iii) $\triangle 3 \rightarrow \triangle 4$: rotation 90° anticlockwise, centre (2, 2).

      (iv) $\triangle 4 \rightarrow \triangle 5$: translation $\begin{pmatrix} -4 \\ -4 \end{pmatrix}$.   (v) $\triangle 5 \rightarrow \triangle 6$: rotation 180°, centre $(-2, -6)$.
   (c) Write down the coordinates of the 'pointed ends' of triangles $\triangle 2$, $\triangle 3$, $\triangle 4$, $\triangle 5$ and $\triangle 6$.

6.2 MENTAL ARITHMETIC

In each test the questions are read out by the teacher while all pupils' books are closed. Each question is repeated once and then the answer, and only the answer, is written down. All working is done 'in the head'.

Each test, including the recording of results, should take about 30 minutes.

The tests appear in the book so that pupils can check afterwards to see where they made mistakes.

Test 1

1. Find the cost in pounds of ten books at 35 pence each.

2. Add together £4.20 and 75 pence.

3. What number divided by six gives an answer of eight?

4. I spend £1.60 and pay with £2. My change consists of three coins. What are they?

5. Find the difference between $13\frac{1}{2}$ and 20.

6. Write one centimetre as a fraction of one metre.

7. How many ten pence coins are there in a pile worth £5.60?

8. Ten per cent of the pupils in a school play hockey, 15% play basketball and the rest play football. What percentage play football?

9. In a room of 20 people, three quarters were women. What was the number of women?

10. Four lemons costing eleven pence each are bought with a one pound coin. What is the change?

11. I arrive at the railway station at 5.20 p.m. and my train is due at 6.10 p.m. How long do I have to wait?

12. What number is ten times as big as 0.65?

13. A hockey pitch measures 25 metres by 40 metres. Find the distance around the pitch.

14. Write the number 768 correct to the nearest ten.

15. By how many does a half of 62 exceed 20?

16. How many 2p coins are worth the same as ten 5p coins?

17. What number must be added to $1\frac{1}{4}$ to make $2\frac{1}{2}$?

18. Three books cost six pounds. How much will five books cost?

19. A rubber costs 20 pence. How many can be bought for £2?

20. What number is a hundred times as big as 0.605?

21. Spell the word 'decimal'.

22. Find the average of 12 and 20.

23. A car travelling at 80 kilometres per hour takes 30 minutes for a journey. How long will the car take at 40 kilometres per hour?

24. A certain number multiplied by itself gives 81 as the answer. What is half of that number?

25. The difference between two numbers is 15. One of the numbers is 90. What is the other?

26. How many half-litre glasses can be filled from a vessel containing ten litres?

27. How much will a dozen oranges cost at 20 pence each?

28. What is the biggest number that can be made from the figures 4, 8 and 1?

29. A prize of £400 000 is shared equally between one hundred people. How much does each person receive?

30. If electric cable is 6 pence for 50 cm, how much will 4 metres cost?

Test 2

1. What are 48 twos?

2. How many fives are there in ninety-five?

3. What is 6.30 a.m. on the 24-hour clock?

4. Add together £2.25 and 50 pence.

5. I go shopping with £2.80 and buy a magazine for ninety pence. How much money have I left?

6. Change $2\frac{1}{2}$ feet into inches.

7. Write in figures the number 'five million, eighteen thousand and one.'

8. How many 20 pence biros can be bought for £3?

9. Work out 1% of £600.

10. A packet of 10 small cakes costs 35 pence. How much does each cake cost?

11. Add eight to 9 fives.

12. A packet of flour weighing 2400 grams is divided into three equal parts. How heavy is each part?

13. Add together 7, 23 and 44.

14. A car does 40 miles per gallon of petrol. How far does the car travel on seven gallons of petrol?

15. How many twenty pence coins are needed to make eight pounds?

16. A certain butterfly lives for just 96 hours. How many days is this?

17. What number is 25 more than 37?

18. Find the average of 2, 5 and 8.

19. Pears cost eleven pence each. How many can I buy for sixty pence?

20. How many minutes are there in eight hours?

21. What number is twice as big as seventy-nine?

22. How many minutes are there between 6.25 p.m. and 8.00 p.m.?

23. Write one-fifth as a decimal.

24. Which is the larger: 0.7, or 0.071?

25. If a woman earns £8.40 per hour, how much does she earn in ten hours?

26. A car costing £2500 is reduced by £45. What is the new price?

27. How many half kilogram packets of sugar can be filled from a large bowl containing 32 kilograms?

28. My daily paper costs 15 pence and I buy the paper six days a week. What is my weekly bill?

29. A car journey of 110 miles took two hours. What was the average speed of the car?

30. How many days will there by in February 1993?

Test 3

1. What number is fifteen more than fifty-five?

2. What is a tenth of 2400?

3. What is twenty times forty-five?

4. Write in figures the number ten thousand, seven hundred and five.

5. A play lasting $2\frac{1}{4}$ hours starts at half-past eight. When does it finish?

6. What number is fifty-five less than 300?

7. How many twelves are there in 240?

8. A book costs £1.95. How much change do I receive from a five pound note?

9. Find the cost of eight biros at 22 pence each.

10. What four coins make 61 pence?

11. Work out $\frac{1}{2}$ plus $\frac{1}{4}$ and give the answer as a decimal.

12. A box holds 16 cans. How many boxes are needed for 80 cans?

13. If the 25th of December is a Tuesday, what day of the week is the first of January?

14. By how much is two kilos more than 500 g?

15. Write down fifteen thousand and fifty pence in pounds and pence.

16. The sides of a square field measure 160 metres. Find the total distance around the field.

17. A three-piece suite costing £970 is reduced by £248. What is the new price?

18. A bingo prize of £150 000 is shared equally between six people. How much does each person receive?

19. Ice creams cost twenty-four pence each. How many can I buy with one pound?

20. A bag contains 22 five pence coins. How much is in the bag?

21. How many pounds are there in two stones?

22. A wine merchant puts 100 bottles in crates of 12. How many crates does he need?

23. Add together 73 and 18.

24. What is 5% of £120?

25. Peaches cost fourteen pence each. How much do I pay for seven peaches?

26. A toy costs 54 pence. Find the change from a five pound note.

27. A boy goes to and from school by bus and a ticket costs 33 pence each way. How much does he spend in a five-day week?

28. In your purse, you have two ten pound notes, three five pound notes and seven one pound coins. How much have you got altogether?

29. What are eighty twelves?

30. Sweets cost 72 pence a pound. How much do I pay if I buy four ounces of sweets?

Test 4

1. What is the change from a £10 note for goods costing £1.95?

2. Add 12 to 7 nines.

3. How many 20 pence coins are needed to make £5?

4. A pile of 100 sheets of paper is 10 cm thick. How thick is each sheet?

5. Lemons cost 7 pence each or 60 pence a dozen. How much is saved by buying a dozen instead of 12 separate lemons?

6. How many weeks are there in two years?

7. What is 1% of £40?

8. How much more than £92 is £180?

9. My watch reads five past 6. It is 15 minutes fast. What is the correct time?

10. If a pint of beer costs 82p, how much does a man pay for a round of 10 pints?

11. A cycle track is 800 metres long. How far do I go in kilometres if I complete 5 laps of the track?

12. A train travels at an average speed of 30 mph for $1\frac{1}{2}$ hours. How far does it travel?

13. I go shopping with £5 and buy 3 items at 25 pence each. How much money have I left?

14. From one thousand and seven take away nine.

15. If I can cycle a mile in 3 minutes, how many miles can I cycle in one hour?

16. How many millimetres are there in 20 cm?

17. A metal rod 90 cm long is cut into four equal parts. How long is one part?

18. Find the cost of fifteen items at 5 pence each.

19. A 2 pence coin is about 2 mm thick. How many coins are in a pile which is 2 cm high?

20. Add up the first four odd numbers.

21. Add up the first four even numbers.

22. My daily paper costs 18 pence. I pay for it with a £10 note. What change do I receive?

23. A film starts at 8.53 p.m. and finishes at 9.15 p.m. How long is the film?

24. We finish school at twenty to four. What is that on the 24-hour clock?

25. Add together £2.34 and £5.60.

26. What is 10% of £7?

27. How many 2 pence coins are needed to make £4?

28. 35% of a class prefer BBC1 and 30% prefer ITV. What percentage prefer the other two channels?

29. How many minutes is it between 6.20 p.m. and 8.00 p.m.?

30. What is the cost of 1000 books at £2.50 each?

Test 5

1. How many minutes are there in 6 hours?

2. Add together £8.65 and 40 pence.

3. Find the average of 6, 14 and 16.

4. A packet of 30 sweets costs 45 pence. How much is each sweet?

5. The time by my watch is twenty past nine. What is the correct time if my watch is 15 minutes slow?

6. A ship was due at noon on Tuesday but arrived at 5.00 p.m. on Wednesday. How many hours late was the ship?

7. How many days are there in 20 weeks?

8. From nine times eight take away fifteen.

9. On a coach forty-one out of fifty people are men. What percentage is this?

10. Electric cable costs 90 pence per foot. How much do I pay for 4 inches of cable?

11. Spell the word 'diagonal'.

12. Two angles of a triangle are 65° and 20°. What is the third angle?

13. How many 5 pence coins are needed to make 120 pence?

14. If a man earns £2.25 per hour, how much does he earn in 4 hours?

15. A T.V. programme lasting 55 minutes starts at 20 minutes to seven. When does it finish?

16. How much less than 260 is 16?

17. Seven apples costing twelve pence each are bought with a £5 note. What is the change?

18. Add 24 to eleven sixes.

19. How many millimetres are there in $5\frac{1}{2}$ cm?

20. A car travels at an average speed of 30 mph. How far does it travel in $1\frac{1}{2}$ hours?

21. What is the perimeter of a square of area 36 cm^2?

22. A rod of length 370 cm is cut in half. How long is each piece?

23. A half is a third of a certain number. What is the number?

24. About how much does a man earn in a week if he is paid £10 000 a year?

25. Between midnight and 3 a.m. the temperature falls by 7°C. If the temperature at midnight was 5°C, what was the temperature at 3 a.m.?

26. An egg box holds 6 eggs. How many boxes are needed for 92 eggs?

27. A car costing £7600 is reduced in price by £750. What is the new price?

28. A man smokes 40 cigarettes a day and cigarettes cost £1.30 for 20. How much does he spend in 3 days?

29. By how much is half a metre longer than 1 millimetre? (answer in mm).

30. Write in figures the number 'eight million, twenty-seven thousand and ten'.

Test 6

1. What is a half of two thousand one hundred?

2. The time by the town hall clock is half-past three but the clock is eight minutes slow. What is the correct time?

3. If I have 65 pence change from a ten pound note, how much have I spent?

4. Find the average of 27 and 31.

5. Work out 10% of £65.

6. For homework a teacher sets questions 30 to 50 inclusive. How many questions is that?

7. How many millimetres are there in 40 centimetres?

8. Between noon and midnight the temperature falls by 20 °C. The temperature at noon is 12 °C. What is the temperature at midnight?

9. How many days are there in thirty weeks?

10. Write down a thousand pence in pounds.

11. What number is three times as big as fifty-one?

12. A man is paid £40 a week. About how much is that in a year?

13. An egg box holds six eggs. How many boxes are needed for seventy eggs?

14. From eight times seven take away eleven.

15. Five pounds of carrots cost one pound. How much do they cost per pound?

16. How many minutes are there in four hours?

17. Spell the word 'equation'.

18. What four coins make 62 pence?

19. Add together £2.90 and 65 pence.

20. A man died in 1981 aged 65. In what year was he born?

21. A tennis match lasting two and a quarter hours starts at a quarter past two. When does it finish?

22. The single fare for a journey is £7 and a day return is £11.25. How much is saved by buying a day return rather than two singles?

23. By how much is one kilogram more than one hundred grams?

24. What is a half of three hundred and ten?

25. Two angles of a triangle are 90° and 41°. What is the third angle?

26. How many weeks are there in two years?

27. A three-piece suite costing £950 is reduced by £280. What is the new price?

28. A train is due to arrive at 6.15 a.m. What is this time on the 24-hour clock?

29. A car travels at 60 miles per hour for $2\frac{1}{2}$ hours. How far does it go?

30. A ship was due to arrive at 7.00 p.m. on Friday, but arrived at 3.00 p.m. on Saturday. How many hours late was it?

Test 7

1. Find the average of 22 and 32.
2. If a man earns £2.50 per hour, how much does he earn in 5 hours?
3. How many fives are there in eighty?
4. What number is twice as big as eighty-five?
5. Write in figures the number three million seventeen thousand and four.
6. A ship sails for five days. How many hours is this?
7. What is 7.22 p.m. on the 24-hour clock?
8. How many two pence coins are needed to make five pounds?
9. Write three hundredths as a decimal.
10. A television costing £340 is reduced by £95. What is the new price?
11. A man goes shopping with £10 and buys three items at seventy pence each. How much money has he left?
12. A packet of twenty chocolates costs 90 pence. How much does each chocolate cost?
13. A car does 30 miles per gallon of petrol. How much petrol is used on a journey of 15 miles?
14. How many minutes are there in $3\frac{1}{2}$ hours?
15. After using slug pellets a gardener kills four-fifths of the slugs in his garden. What percentage is left?
16. Add together £7.85 and 29 pence.
17. Add twelve to 9 nines.
18. What is 10% of £4?
19. How many 40 pence rulers can be bought for £2?
20. Pears cost nine pence each. How many can I buy for one pound?
21. A metal rod of length 350 cm is cut in half. How long is each piece?
22. How many minutes are there between 11.30 a.m. and 2.00 p.m.?
23. Add together 9, 22 and 30.
24. How many half pint glasses can be filled from a barrel containing 19 pints?
25. If a man earns £4.50 per hour, how much does he earn in three hours?
26. A packet of crisps costs 15 pence and a boy eats three packets every day. How much does he spend in ten days?
27. A train took five hours to travel a distance of 400 miles. What was the average speed of the train?
28. A gallon of a precious liquid costs £100. About how much is this per pint?
29. A woman died in 1983 aged 75. In what year was she born?
30. By how much is three kilometres longer than three metres?

Test 8

1. What number multiplied by itself gives an answer of 81?
2. Add together six 50 pences and four 20 pences and give the answer in pounds.
3. If I change £10 into 20 pence coins, how many will I get?
4. The profit on a drink is 20 pence. How many must be sold to make a profit of £10?
5. What number divided by 8 gives an answer of 9?
6. What is the angle between the hands of a clock at 3 o'clock?
7. What is the smallest number that can be made using each of the figures 4, 8 and 1 once only?
8. Find the difference between $11\frac{1}{2}$ and 20.
9. Rewrite as an ordinary number 4×10^3.
10. Write one millimetre as a fraction of one metre.
11. How many 2p coins are worth the same as twenty 5p coins?
12. What number equals nine dozen?
13. Which is the larger fraction: $\frac{7}{10}$ or $\frac{3}{5}$?
14. If fish costs £4.60 per kilo, how much will I pay for 250 g?
15. What is the smallest number which must be added to 41 to make it exactly divisible by 8?
16. How many 50 ml glasses can be filled from a one litre bottle?
17. Write in figures the number 'fifteen thousand and twenty-four'.

18. A pencil costs 5 pence. How many can be bought for £1.20?

19. The difference between two numbers is 15. One of the numbers is 22. What is the other number?

20. A pile of 15 boxes is 3 metres high. What is the depth of each box?

21. In a group of 30 people, $\frac{2}{5}$ were men. What was the number of women?

22. A spark plug for a car costs 75p. How much does a set of six plugs cost?

23. A rectangular pane of glass is 3 feet long and 2 feet wide. Glass costs £1.50 per square foot. How much will the pane cost?

24. The single fare for a journey is £7 and a day return is £9.50. How much is saved by buying a day return rather than two singles?

25. The weekly rent for a flat is £21. Eight weeks rent must be paid in advance. How much is that?

26. How many 15 pence rulers can be bought for £1?

27. Electricity costs 6 pence per unit. How much would you pay for 300 units?

28. How many weeks is 98 days?

29. How long is it between 7.45 p.m. and 9.30 p.m.?

30. One-fifth of my wages is taken in deductions. What percentage have I got left?

Test 9

1. Find the cost of eight stamps at nine pence each.

2. What number is 32 more than 80?

3. Write down six hundred pence in pounds.

4. Apples cost 12 pence each. How many can I buy for 80p?

5. What are nineteen twos?

6. If the 8th of December is a Tuesday, what day of the week is the 18th of December?

7. A sum of £132 is shared equally between twelve people. How much does each person receive?

8. A television programme lasts for two and a quarter hours and starts at half-past six. When does it finish?

9. What four coins make seventy-two pence?

10. Work out $\frac{1}{2}$ take away $\frac{1}{4}$ and give the answer as a decimal.

11. What is a half of a half of 38?

12. What is a quarter of a half of 800?

13. By how much is four metres more than four centimetres? (answer in cm).

14. How many twos are there in a thousand?

15. Spell the word 'parallel'.

16. Write in figures the number thirty thousand and ten.

17. How many inches are there in a foot?

18. A house priced at £60 000 is reduced by £4500. What is the new price?

19. What number is eight times as big as fifty?

20. How many pints are there in a gallon?

21. Spell the word 'circumference'.

22. A square has an area of 144 m². How long is each side of the square?

23. Add together 9, 16 and 70.

24. A calculator costs £3.74. Find the change from a ten pound note.

25. Rulers cost ten pence each. How much will two dozen rulers cost?

26. A boy eats three packets of crisps a day and crisps cost 15 pence a packet. How much does he spend on crisps in two days?

27. Add together 74 and 88.

28. Work out 25% of £64.

29. What are fifteen 20's?

30. Which is larger: 0.3 or $\frac{1}{4}$?

Test 10

1. What is the change from a £20 note for goods costing £4.35?

2. Add 12 to 7 nines.

3. How many 20 pence coins are needed to make £20?

4. A pile of 100 sheets of paper is 1 cm thick. How thick is each sheet?

5. Tomatoes cost 6 pence each or 60 pence a dozen. How much is saved by buying a dozen instead of 12 separate tomatoes?

6. How many weeks are there in three years?

7. What is 1% of £60?

8. How much more than £85 is £150?

9. My watch reads five past 7. It is 20 minutes fast. What is the correct time?

10. If a pint of beer costs 85p, how much does a man pay for a round of 10 pints?

11. A cycle track is 600 metres long. How far do I go in km if I complete 5 laps of the track?

12. A train travels at an average speed of 40 mph for $2\frac{1}{2}$ hours. How far does it travel?

13. I go shopping with £5 and buy 3 items at 60 pence each. How much money have I left?

14. From one thousand and two take away three.

15. If I can cycle a mile in four minutes, how many miles can I cycle in one hour?

16. How many millimetres are there in $15\frac{1}{2}$ cm?

17. A metal rod 170 cm long is cut into four equal parts. How long is one part?

18. Find the cost of fifteen items at 4 pence each.

19. A 2 pence coin is about 2 mm thick. How many coins are in a pile which is 1 cm high?

20. Add up the first five odd numbers.

21. Add up the first five even numbers.

22. My daily paper costs 23 pence. I pay for it with a £10 note. What change do I receive?

23. A film starts at 8.47 p.m. and finishes at 9.13 p.m. How long is the film?

24. We finish school at twenty to four. What is that on the 24-hour clock?

25. Add together £2.34 and £5.21.

26. What is 10% of £5.

27. How many 2 pence coins are needed to make £50?

28. 25% of a class prefer BBC1 and 30% prefer ITV. What percentage prefer the other two channels?

29. How many minutes is it between 2.15 p.m. and 4.20 p.m.?

30. What is the cost of 100 books at £4.25 each?

6.3 SYMMETRY

(a) Line symmetry

The letter M has one line of symmetry, shown dotted.

(b) Rotational symmetry

The shape may be turned about O into three identical positions. It has rotational symmetry of order three.

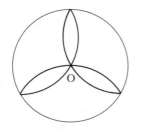

Exercise 3

For each shape state:
(a) the number of lines of symmetry
(b) the order of rotational symmetry.

1.

2.
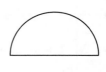

3.

4.

5.

6.

19.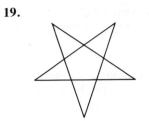

20.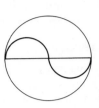

7.

8.

21.

22.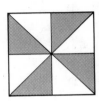

9.

10.

23.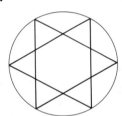

24.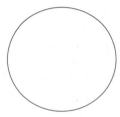

11.

12.

13.

14.

15.

16.

17.

18.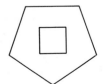

6.4 FLOW DIAGRAMS

Exercise 4

Copy each flow diagram and put each of the
numbers 1, 2, 3, 4, 5, 6, 7 in at the box marked
N. Work out what number would be printed in
each case.

1.

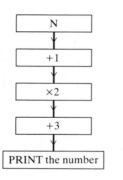

2.

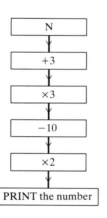

3.

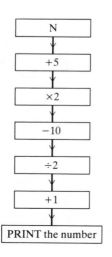

4.

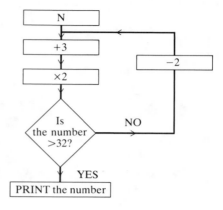

5.

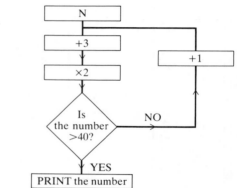

6.

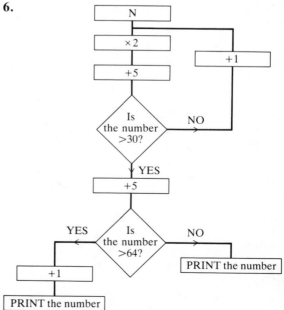

In questions **7** and **8**, use N = 1, 2, 3, . . . 9.

7.

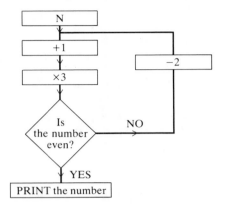

8.

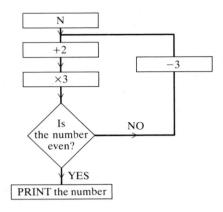

Find the operation

Exercise 5

In the flow charts, the boxes A, B, C and D each contain a single mathematical operation (like +5, ×4, −15, ÷2).

Look at flow charts (i) and (ii) together and work out what is the same operation which will replace A. Complete the flow chart by replacing B, C and D.

Now copy and complete each flow chart on the right, using the same operations.

1. (i) 1 → A → 8 → B → 16 → C → 5 → D → 15

(ii) 3 → A → 10 → B → 20 → C → 9 → D → 27

(a) 4 → A → ? → B → ? → C → ? → D → ?

(b) 5 → A → ? → B → ? → C → ? → D → ?

(c) ? → A → ? → B → 28 → C → ? → D → ?

(d) ? → A → 16 → B → ? → C → ? → D → ?

(e) ? → A → ? → B → ? → C → 25 → D → ?

(f) ? → A → ? → B → ? → C → ? → D → 87

2. (i) 2 → A → 4 → B → 19 → C → 12 → D → 3

(ii) 4 → A → 8 → B → 23 → C → 16 → D → 4

(a) 6 → A → ? → B → ? → C → ? → D → ?

(b) 3 → A → ? → B → ? → C → ? → D → ?

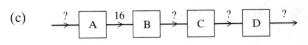

(c) ? → A → 16 → B → ? → C → ? → D → ?

(d) ? → A → ? → B → 35 → C → ? → D → ?

(e) ? → A → ? → B → ? → C → ? → D → $2\frac{1}{2}$

(f) ? → A → ? → B → ? → C → ? → D → 8

3. (i) 2 → ☐ → 17 → ☐ → 34 → ☐ → 12 → ☐ → 3

(ii) 4 → ☐ → 19 → ☐ → 38 → ☐ → 16 → ☐ → 4

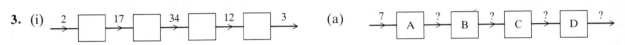

(a) 7 → A → ? → B → ? → C → ? → D → ?

(b) 10 → A → ? → B → ? → C → ? → D → ?

(c) ? → A → ? → B → 62 → C → ? → D → ?

(d) ? → A → $15\frac{1}{2}$ → B → ? → C → ? → D → ?

(e) ? → A → ? → B → ? → C → 208 → D → ?

(f) ? → A → ? → B → ? → C → ? → D → 14

4. (i) 2 → ☐ → 4 → ☐ → 12 → ☐ → 2 → ☐ → 1

(ii) 3 → ☐ → 9 → ☐ → 27 → ☐ → 17 → ☐ → $8\frac{1}{2}$

(a) 4 → A → 16 → B → ? → C → ? → D → ?

(b) 5 → A → ? → B → ? → C → ? → D → ?

(c) ? → A → ? → B → 108 → C → ? → D → ?

(d) ? → A → ? → B → ? → C → 182 → D → ?

(e) ? → A → ? → B → 3 → C → ? → D → ?

(f) ? → A → ? → B → ? → C → ? → D → 145

Think about it 2

Project 1   **MAXIMUM BOX**

(a) You have a square sheet of card 24 cm by 24 cm. You can make a box (without a lid) by cutting squares from the corners and folding up the sides.

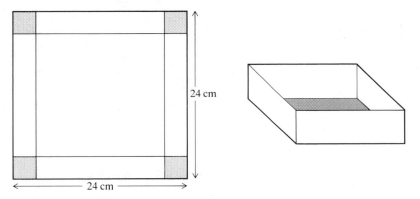

What size corners should you cut out so that the volume of the box is as large as possible? Try different sizes for the corners and record the results in the form of a table:

Length of the side of the corner square (cm)	Dimensions of the open box (cm)	Volume of the open box (cm³)
1	22 × 22 × 1	484
2		
⋮		
⋮		

(b) Now consider boxes made from different sized cards: 15 cm by 15 cm and 20 cm by 20 cm. What size corners should you cut out this time so that the volume of the box is as large as possible?

(c) Finally investigate the situation when the card is not square. For a rectangular card 20 cm by 12 cm what size corners should you cut out for maximum volume?

Exercise A

1. How many shares of an electronics company, each costing 74p, can be bought for £444?

2. The train fare to York is £5.40 for an adult and £2.20 for a child. How much change will a man get from £20 if he is taking his wife and three children?

3. A jet is flying at 720 km/h.
   (a) How many metres will it travel in one hour?
   (b) How many metres will it travel in one second?

4. Ten posts are equally spaced in a straight line. It is 450 m from the first to the tenth post. What is the distance between successive posts?

5. A journey by boat takes 2 hours 47 minutes. How long will it take at half the speed?

6. Copy the following tables and write down the next *two* lines
   (a) $2^2 = 1^2 + 3$
          $3^2 = 2^2 + 5$
          $4^2 = 3^2 + 7$
          $5^2 = 4^2 + 9$

   (b) $3^2 = 4 + 1^2 + 2^2$
          $5^2 = 12 + 2^2 + 3^2$
          $7^2 = 24 + 3^2 + 4^2$
          $9^2 = 40 + 4^2 + 5^2$

7. Change the fractions $\frac{3}{5}$ and $\frac{2}{3}$ into decimals. Which fraction is larger?

8. Three girls are 127 cm, 136 cm and 133 cm in height.
   (a) What is their average height?
   (b) When another girl joins them, the new average height is 134 cm. How tall is the fourth girl?

9. (a) A rectangular floor 5 m by 6 m is to be covered with square tiles, each of side length 50 cm. How many tiles will be required?
   (b) If the same floor is covered with smaller tiles of side 25 cm, how many are needed now?

10. A motor cycle averages 75 miles to a gallon of petrol which costs £1.85 per gallon. If the motor cycle goes 24 000 miles in the year, calculate:
    (a) The number of gallons of petrol used
    (b) The cost of the petrol.

Project 2   **REFLECTIONS**

Copy each drawing onto squared paper and then draw the reflection of the object in the mirror line shown by the dotted line. When you have done these, make up pictures of your own and draw their reflections.

1.

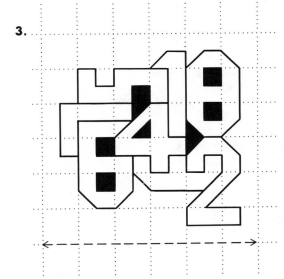

2.

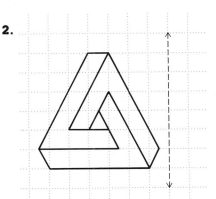

3.

4.

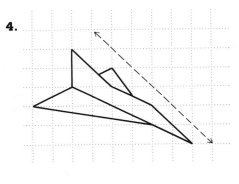

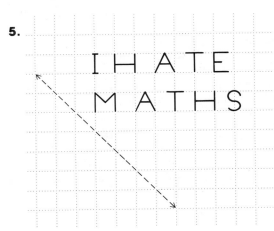

5.

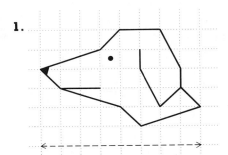

Exercise B

1. Ann weighs 24 kg and her father weighs three times as much.
   (a) How heavy is Ann's father?
   (b) How heavy is Ann's sister, Susan, if their father is four times as heavy as Susan?

2. If 6 kg of flour costs £2.04, how much will it cost for 10 kg?

3. The room shown is to be fitted with carpet tiles. Each tile is 1 m square and costs £8.50.

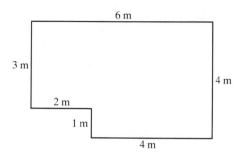

   (a) How many tiles are needed?
   (b) What is the total cost?
   (c) How many tiles were used in another room which cost £425 to cover with tiles?

4. (a) Increase £80 by 25%.
   (b) Decrease 150 kg by 5%.
   (c) Decrease 80 cm by 40%.

5. What fraction of £2 is
   (a) 20p   (b) 50p   (c) 2p?

6. Of 60 people travelling on a boat, 48 can swim. What percentage of the people is this?

7. V.A.T. of 15% is added to the price of an article costing £12.60.
   (a) How much V.A.T. was paid?
   (b) How much did the article cost, including tax?

8. Seven fig rolls together weigh 560 g. A calorie guide shows that 10 g of fig roll contains 52 calories.
   (a) How much does one fig roll weigh?
   (b) How many calories are there in 1 g of fig roll?
   (c) How many calories are there in one fig roll?

9. An aircraft is flying at an average speed of 750 km/h.
   (a) How far will it fly in 2 hours 30 minutes?
   (b) How long will it take to fly 1650 km?

10. A cinema has 30 rows of seats, with 15 seats in each row. The price of tickets for the first five rows is £3 per seat. All other seats cost £2 each.
    (a) How many seats are there in the cinema?
    (b) Calculate the income from the sale of tickets for 10 performances if all the seats are sold.

Project 3   CROSS NUMBERS

Draw four copies of the pattern below and fill them in using the clues.

1		2	▓	3		▓	4
	▓	5				▓	
6			▓			7	
	▓	8	9			▓	▓
▓	10			▓	11		
12		▓	13	14		▓	▓
	▓	15	▓	16		17	18
19			▓		▓	20	

Part A

Across

1. 111 × 7
3. 145 ÷ 5
5. 15 924 ÷ 4
6. 5 × 121
7. 326 − 248
8. 5148 ÷ 6
10. 152 × 4
11. 37 × 11
12. 603 ÷ 9
13. 7 × 124
16. 8730 ÷ 5
19. 398 + 174
20. 0.7^2 × 100

Down

1. 22 683 ÷ 3
2. 73.58 × 1000
3. 312 × 9
4. 829 − 671
7. 7 ÷ 0.01
9. 98 × 6
10. 469 ÷ 7
11. 600 − 113
12. 123 × 5
14. 486 + 129
15. 0.2 × 0.6 × 100
17. 812 − 768
18. 0.069 × 500 × 2

Part B

Across

1. $3368 \div 4$
3. $323 - 249$
5. 814×6
6. $6 \times 7 \times 8$
7. $5 \times 12 - 3$
8. $11^2 - 1^2$
10. $411 + 98$
11. 0.724×10^3
12. $3^2 + 7^2$
13. $8 \times 9 \times 10$
16. 624×11
19. $2056 \div 8$
20. $611 - 564$

Down

1. $24\,411 \div 3$
2. 4922×5
3. $46\,980 \div 6$
4. 3.17×10^2
7. 58×9
9. $15 \times 20 - 3$
10. Half of 116
11. $1000 - 292$
12. 74×8
14. $1325 \div 5$
15. $3^2 + 2^3$
17. $2 \times 2 \times 2 \times 2 \times 2 \times 2$
18. 0.0047×10^4

Part C

Across

1. $(621 + 184) \div 5$
3. Number of inches in a yard
5. $38\,748 \div 6$
6. $6 \times 12 \times 12$
7. Next in the sequence
   60, 52, 44, 36, . . .
8. Solve $4x - 11 = 1429$
10. $5096 \div 8$
11. $252 + 187 + 366$
12. 1% of 2500
13. Solve $3x - 5 = 367$
16. $4000 - 889$
19. $10^3 - 1^3$
20. Next in the sequence
    41, 45, 50, 56, . . .

Down

1. $2588 - 803$
2. $49\,299 \div 3$
3. 25% of 14 000
4. Double 84 plus treble 60
7. $1820 \div 7$
9. $824 - 153$
10. 10% of 650
11. $30^2 - 59$
12. 0.259×10^3
14. $9 \times (15 + 11)$
15. Next in the sequence
    11, 18, 25, 32, . . .
17. Number of ounces in a pound.
18. Solve $2x + 3 = 29$

Part D

Across

1. $427 + 165$
3. Prime number between 32 and 40
5. 742×7
6. $1880 \div 5$
7. $10^2 - 1^2$
8. $882 - 56$
10. 20% of 1200
11. Number of minutes between 1040 and 1305.
12. A quarter of 156
13. $5067 \div 9$
16. $2316 + 1842 + 4317$
19. 42×11
20. Next in the sequence
    23, 26, 31, 38, . . .

Down

1. $4658 + 874$
2. $154\,104 \div 6$
3. $4274 - 318$
4. $4719 \div 11$
7. 76 less than a thousand
9. $(9 - 4) \times (50 - 9)$
10. Number of minutes between 1152 and 1221
11. Average of 127, 117 and 158
12. 3% of 10800
14. $(1507 \times 5) \div (50 - 39)$
15. Next in the sequence
    $1\frac{1}{2}$, 3, 6, . . .
17. 2% of 3700
18. An eighth of 456

Exercise C

Work out the value indicated by the arrow.

1.

2.

3.

4.

5.

6.

7.

8.

9.

10.

11.

12.

13.

14.

15.

16.

17.

18.

19.

20.

21.

22.

23.

24.

25.

26.

27.

28.

29.

30.

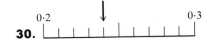

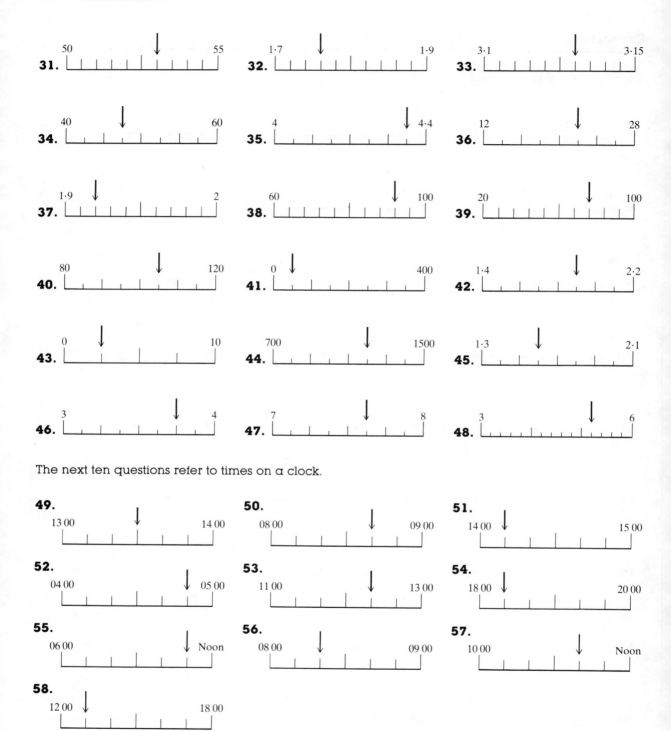

The next ten questions refer to times on a clock.

Project 4

CALCULATOR WORDS

On a calculator the number 4915 looks like the word 'SIGH' when the calculator is held upside down.

Find the words given by the clues below.

1. $221 \times 7 \times 5$ (Sounds like 'cell')
2. $5 \times 601 \times 5 \times 3$ (Wet blow)
3. $88^2 - 6$ (Ringer)
4. $0.9 \times 5900 - 1$ (Leaves)
5. $62^2 - (4 \times 7 \times 5)$ (Nothing to it)
6. $0.88^2 - \frac{1}{1000}$ (O Hell)
7. $(5 \times 7 \times 10^3) + (3 \times 113)$ (Gaggle)
8. $44^2 +$ Half of 67 682 (Readable)
9. $5 \times 3 \times 37 \times 1000 - 1420$ (Stick in mind)
10. $3200 - 1320 \div 11$ (Woodwind)
11. $48^4 + 8929$ (Deceitful dame)
12. $31^2 \times 32^2 - 276^2 + 30$ (Not a twig)
13. $(130 \times 135) + (23 \times 3 \times 11 \times 23)$ (Wobbly)
14. $164 \times 166^2 + 734$ (Almost big)
15. $8794^2 + 25 \times 342.28 + 120 \times 25$ (Thin skin)
16. $0.08 - (3^2 \div 10^4)$ (Ice house)
17. $235^2 - (4 \times 36.5)$ (Shiny surface)
18. $(80^2 + 60^2) \times 3 + 81^2 + 12^2 + 3013$ (ship gunge)
19. $3 \times 17 \times (329^2 + 2 \times 173)$ (Unlimbed)
20. $230 \times 230\frac{1}{2} + 30$ (Fit feet)
21. $33 \times 34 \times 35 + 15 \times 3$ (Beleaguer)
22. $0.32^2 + \frac{1}{1000}$ (Did he or didn't he?)
23. $(23 \times 24 \times 25 \times 26) + (3 \times 11 \times 10^3) - 20$ (Help)
24. $(16^2 + 16)^2 - (13^2 - 2)$ (Slander)
25. $(3 \times 661)^2 - (3^6 + 22)$ (Pester)
26. $(22^2 + 29.4) \times 10; (3.03^2 - 0.02^2) \times 100^2$ (Four words) (Goliath)
27. $1.25 \times 0.2^6 + 0.2^2$ (Tissue time)
28. $(710 + (1823 \times 4)) \times 4$ (Liquor)
29. $(3^3)^2 + 2^2$ (Wriggler)
30. $14 + (5 \times (83^2 + 110))$ (Bigger than a duck)
31. $2 \times 3 \times 53 \times 10^4 + 9$ (Opposite to hello, almost!)
32. $(177 \times 179 \times 182) + (85 \times 86) - 82$ (Good salesman)

Exercise D

1. A wall measuring 3.40 m by 2 m is to be covered with square tiles of side 20 cm.
  (a) How many tiles are needed?
  (b) If the tiles cost £2.60 for ten, how much will it cost?

2. It needs 80 g of flour to make 24 small biscuits. How much flour is needed to make 36 of these biscuits?

3. Work out $\frac{2}{5} + \frac{3}{4}$, giving your answer in its simplest form.

4. Calculate the area of the shape below.

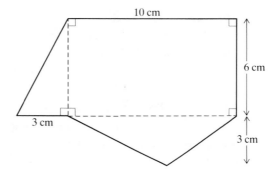

5. Discount at the rate of 12p in the £ is allowed on all articles in a sale. In this sale, what is the sale price of:
  (a) an article with a normal price of £5
  (b) an article with a normal price of £12

6. A shirt and a tie cost £11. If the shirt cost £7 more than the tie, what is the cost of each item?

7. Work out: a) $\frac{2}{3} \times \frac{1}{5}$;   b) $\frac{5}{8} + \frac{1}{4}$;   c) $\frac{1}{6} - \frac{1}{18}$.

8. It is correct that $8 - 2 \times 3 - 1 = 1$
  (Remember x, ÷ before +, −)
  Also $(8 - 2) \times 3 - 1 = 17$
  (Brackets first)
  By putting either one or two pairs of brackets in the lefthand side, show how the correct answer can be
  (a) 4   (b) 12   (c) 3

9. $9 + 2 \times 4 - 3 = 14$
  Put either one or two pairs of brackets in the lefthand side so that the answer can be
  (a) 41   (b) 11

10. $12 - 5 \times 2 + 4 = 6$
  Put either one or two pairs of brackets in the lefthand side so that the answer can be
  (a) 42   (b) 18   (c) −18   (d) −2

Project 5   BALANCING

In this project □, △, ○ and ∗ represent weights which are always balanced.

1. (a) 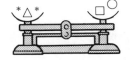   (b)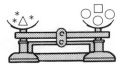

(c)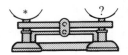

How many ○'s?

2. (a) 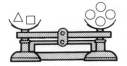   (b)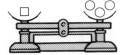

(c)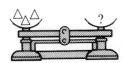

How many ○'s?

3. (a) ○ ○ □ = ∗ ∗
   (b) □ □ ○ = ∗ ∗ ○
   (c) □ = How many ○'s?

4. (a) □ ○ ○ = △ □ □ □
   (b) □ □ □ ○ = △ △ □
   (c) □ ○ = △ □
   (d) ○ = How many □'s?

5. (a) □ □ = ○ △
   (b) ○ ○ ○ □ = □ △
   (c) ○ □ □ □ = △ △ ○
   (d) □ = How many ○'s?

6. (a) ○ ○ □ = ∗ ○
   (b) ∗ ∗ = ○ ○ ○
   (c) □ ∗ = ○ ○
   (d) ∗ = How many □'s?

7. (a) ○ □ □ = △ ∗
   (b) ∗ ∗ ∗ = △ △
   (c) ○ □ = △
   (d) △ △ △ △ = How many □'s?

8. (a) ○ □ = △
   (b) ○ = □ ∗
   (c) ○ ○ □ = △ ∗ ∗
   (d) □ = How many ∗'s?

Exercise E

1. Change the following fractions to decimals and find the odd one out:

$\frac{3}{5}, \frac{39}{65}, \frac{33}{55}, \frac{36}{54}, \frac{27}{45}$.

2. Find the odd one out: $\frac{98}{112}, \frac{63}{72}, \frac{7}{8}, \frac{119}{138}, \frac{105}{120}$

3. Find the odd one out: $\frac{40}{48}, \frac{5}{6}, \frac{75}{90}, \frac{60}{72}, \frac{95}{115}$

4. Find the odd one out: $\frac{45}{144}, \frac{75}{240}, \frac{135}{435}, \frac{105}{336}, \frac{5}{16}$

5. Find the odd one out: $\frac{56}{96}, \frac{7}{12}, \frac{84}{144}, \frac{147}{252}, \frac{217}{370}$

6. Find the odd one out: $\frac{99}{187}, \frac{135}{255}, \frac{153}{289}, \frac{189}{356}, \frac{9}{17}$

7. Use a calculator to change the fractions to decimals and then arrange the fractions in order of size, smallest first.

   (a) $\frac{7}{8}, \frac{17}{20}, \frac{27}{32}$.
   (b) $\frac{21}{100}, \frac{9}{40}, \frac{1}{5}$
   (c) $\frac{5}{6}, \frac{6}{7}, \frac{3}{4}$

   (d) $\frac{2}{3}, \frac{8}{11}, \frac{5}{9}$
   (e) $\frac{7}{9}, \frac{11}{12}, \frac{3}{4}, \frac{13}{15}$
   (f) $\frac{3}{5}, \frac{15}{19}, \frac{17}{23}$

   (g) $\frac{5}{11}, \frac{4}{13}, \frac{7}{19}, \frac{17}{37}$

8. Using a calculator I divided two whole numbers under 10 and found the answer was 0.7777777.
   What were the two numbers?

9. Using a calculator I divided two whole numbers under 10 and found the answer was 0.8571428.
   What were the two numbers?

10. Using a calculator I divided two whole numbers under 15 and found the answer was 0.5833333.
    What were the two numbers?

11. Using a calculator I divided two whole numbers under 20 and found the answer was 0.4705882.
    What were the two numbers?

12. I divided two whole numbers under 12 and found the answer was 1.375.
    What were the two numbers?

13. I divided two whole numbers under 15 and found the answer was 1.444444.
    What were the two numbers?

14. I divided two whole numbers under 15 and found the answer was 1.090909.
    What were the two numbers?

15. I divided two whole numbers under 20 and found the answer was 0.1764705.
    What were the two numbers?

16. I divided two whole numbers under 20 and found the answer was 0.368421.
    What were the two numbers?

Project 6   LARGEST PRODUCT

1. Arrange the digits 1, 2, 3 and 4, one into each box, so that the answer is as large as possible.

2. Arrange the digits 1, 2, 3, 4 and 5, one into each box, so that the answer is as large as possible.

3. What is the largest number which can be found with a single multiplication using each of the digits 1, 2, 3, 4, 5 and 6 once only?

4. What is the largest number which can be found with a single multiplication using each of the digits 1, 2, 3, 4, 5, 6 and 7 once only?

5. What is the largest number which can be found with a single multiplication using each of the digits 1, 2, 3, 4, 5, 6, 7 and 8 once only?

6. Can you find a rule which will help you to answer the questions above?

Exercise F

1. A man hires a car and the car hire company charges £8 per day plus 5p per km travelled.
    (a) How much does it cost to hire a car for three days and drive 500 km?
    (b) How much does it cost to hire a car for seven days and drive 750 km?
    (c) A man hired a car for two days and had to pay £21. How far did he drive?

2. The workers in a bank are offered the choice of two pay rises. Workers can choose either a 4.5% increase on their salaries or they can accept a rise of £250.
    (a) A secretary earns £5260 a year. Which pay rise should she accept?
    (b) A cleaner earns £3140 a year. Which pay rise should he accept?

3. The outline of a 50p coin is shown below.

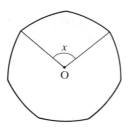

    (a) Draw in any lines of symmetry
    (b) Calculate the size of the angle marked x (O is the centre of the coin).

4. A shopkeeper bought 30 articles for £4.50 and sold them at 20p each. Find the missing numbers below.
    (a) The cost price of each article was *p.
    (b) The total selling price was £ *.
    (c) The total profit was £ *.

5. Every day on his way to school James walks for $\frac{1}{4}$ hour, rides a horse for $\frac{1}{5}$ hour, takes a boat for $\frac{2}{3}$ hour and finally runs the last part in $\frac{3}{10}$ hour. How long is his journey in minutes?

6. The diagram represents a railway siding. Each ● is a junction where a train can turn left or right. A turn to the left has a code 0 and a turn to the right has a code 1.

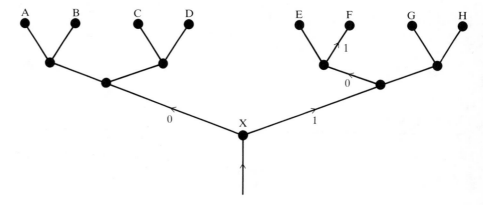

For example, a train starting at X would have code 101 in order to arrive at F.
Copy and complete the table below.

Point	A	B	C	D	E	F	G	H
Code						101		

Project 7   **MATHEMATICAL MAGIC**

Here is a trick which you can perform to demonstrate that you can add even quicker than a calculator!

(a) Ask someone to give a five-digit number with the figures all jumbled up to make it more 'difficult'.

(b) Ask for two more five-digit numbers. You may now have:

$$47563 \quad \ldots A$$
$$25608 \quad \ldots B$$
$$87265 \quad \ldots C$$

(c) Pretend to add two more five-digit numbers at random. In fact choose the fourth number so that when added to number B it makes 99999. Similarly the fifth number is chosen so that when added to number C it also makes 99999. We now have:

$$47563$$
$$25608$$
$$87265$$
$$74391$$
$$12734$$

(d) You now add them together 'in your head' and write down the answer. (Check this on a calculator.)

answer = 247561!

How does it work?

The first digit is always a '2'.

The next five digits are simply 2 less than number A.

i.e. $47563 - 2 = 47561$.

Here is another example.

$$58627$$
$$43817$$
$$38065$$
$$56182$$
$$+ 61934$$
$$\overline{258625}$$

Can you work out why it works?

Now challenge your friends or relatives to an addition race: your brain versus their calculator.

Part 7

7.1 MEAN, MEDIAN AND MODE

Mean

> Five pupils in a class were weighed and their weights were 47 kg, 51 kg, 46 kg, 50 kg and 48 kg.
> Find the mean weight of the pupils.
>
> Mean weight $= \dfrac{47 + 51 + 46 + 50 + 48}{5}$
>
> $= 48.4$ kg

Exercise 1

In questions **1** to **8** find the mean value of the numbers.

1. 7, 3, 8, 9, 4.
2. 2, 5, 1, 7, 6, 3, 2, 5.
3. 7, 8, 9, 4, 6, 8.
4. 6, 6, 6, 6, 6, 6, 6, 6, 6.
5. 1.2, 0.8, 1.1, 0.8, 3.2.
6. 11, 12, 7, 5, 2, 0, 3, 8, 13, 12.
7. −2, −3, 2, 4, −5, 0, 7, −2.
8. 2350, 3164.
9. In a test the marks were
   5, 8, 7, 4, 9, 6, 7, 8, 2, 7.
   Find the mean mark.
10. The speeds of several cars were measured as they travelled down a road. The speeds were (in m.p.h.) 50, 53, 71, 45, 62, 50, 61, 74. Find the mean speed of the cars.
11. Louise claims that she is better at maths than her brother Peter. Louise's last five marks were 63, 72, 58, 84 and 75 and Peter's last four marks were 69, 73, 81 and 70. Find the mean mark for Louise and for Peter. Is Louise better than Peter?

12. (a) Calculate the mean of the numbers
        6, 3, 8, 9, 4, 7, 5.
    (b) Calculate the new mean when the '3' is
        removed.

13. (a) Calculate the mean of the numbers
        8, 11, 5, 2, 9, 1.
    (b) Calculate the new mean when the '8' is
        removed.

14. (a) Calculate the mean of the numbers
        0.8, 1.3, 0.7, 1.4, 2.3, 0.4.
    (b) Calculate the new mean when the '2.3'
        is removed.

15. (a) Calculate the mean of the numbers
        5, 12, 7, 3, 2, 5, 1.
    (b) Calculate the new mean when a '10' is
        added.

16. (a) Calculate the mean of the numbers
        6, 9, 7, 2, 1, 3, 5, 9.
    (b) Calculate the new mean when a '10' and
        a '4' are added.

17. (a) Calculate the mean of the numbers
        13, 6, 8, 5, 3, 8, 6.
    (b) Calculate the new mean when the
        highest number and the lowest number
        are removed.

18. Six boys have heights of 1.53 m, 1.49 m,
    1.60 m, 1.65 m, 1.90 m and 1.43 m.
    (a) Find the mean height of the six boys.
    (b) Find the mean height of the remaining
        five boys when the shortest boy leaves.

19. Seven ladies have weights of 44 kg, 51 kg,
    57 kg, 63 kg, 48 kg, 49 kg and 45 kg.
    (a) Find the mean weight of the seven
        ladies.
    (b) Find the mean weight of the remaining
        five ladies after the lightest and the
        heaviest ladies leave.

20. In a maths test the marks for the boys were
    9, 7, 8, 7, 5 and the marks for the girls were
    6, 3, 9, 8, 2, 2.
    (a) Find the mean mark for the boys.
    (b) Find the mean mark for the girls.
    (c) Find the mean mark for the whole class.

Exercise 2

This exercise is more difficult.

1. The mean of four numbers is 4.1.
   The mean of a different six numbers is 3.2.
   Find (a) the total of the first four numbers.
        (b) the total of the second six numbers.
        (c) the mean of the ten numbers
            altogether.

2. The mean of seven numbers is 3.1.
   The mean of a different three numbers is 4.8.
   Find (a) the total of the first seven numbers.
        (b) the total of the second three
            numbers.
        (c) the mean of the ten numbers
            altogether.

3. The mean of two numbers is 11.6.
   The mean of a different eight numbers is 3.3.
   Find (a) the total of the first two numbers.
        (b) the total of the second eight
            numbers.
        (c) the mean of the ten numbers
            altogether.

4. The mean of four numbers is 3.4.
   The mean of a different five numbers is 1.4.
   Find (a) the total of the first four numbers.
        (b) the total of the second five numbers.
        (c) the mean of the nine numbers
            altogether, correct to 3 s.f.

5. The mean of six numbers is 4.7.
   The mean of a different four numbers is 6.5.
   Calculate the mean of the ten numbers
   altogether.

6. The mean weight of four girls is 48 kg.
   The mean weight of six boys is 53.5 kg.
   Find (a) the total weight of the four girls.
        (b) the total weight of the six boys.
        (c) the mean weight of the group of
            four girls and six boys.

7. The mean height of three men is 1.78 m.
   The mean height of seven women is 1.59 m.
   Find (a) the total height of the men.
        (b) the total height of the women.
        (c) the mean height of the group of
            three men and seven women.

Median

Find the median of the numbers
9, 8, 10, 3, 5, 7, 8, 4, 8.

Arrange the numbers in order of size and
select the one in the middle.
3, 4, 5, 7, 8, 8, 8, 9, 10

↑

The median is 8.

Mode

Find the mode of the numbers
3, 2, 4, 3, 2, 3, 4, 3, 4, 4, 4

The mode is the number which occurs most
often. There are two '2s', four '3s' and five
'4s' so the mode is 4.

Exercise 3

In questions **1** to **14** find the median.
1. 3, 4, 8, 2, 1, 5, 6, 2, 9.
2. 8, 6, 7, 13, 3, 9, 4, 8, 14.
3. 6, 5, 10, 15, 5, 8, 16.
4. 4, 1, 7, 8, 1, 9, 3, 3, 10.
5. 7, 6, 11, 30, 12, 6, 9, 13, 21.
6. 4, 5, 1, 4, 9, 1, 7, 3, 3, 10.
7. 7, 3, 11, 8, 4, 9.
8. 4, 3, 4, 3, 4, 3.
9. 0.5, 0.1, 1.2, 1.3, 1.45.
10. 0.7, 0.35, 0.81, 1.2, 1.9.
11. 1, 7, −3, 3, 8, −1, 5.
12. 2, 0.8, 0.1, $\frac{1}{4}$, $\frac{1}{2}$.
13. $\frac{1}{10}$, 3, $\frac{1}{5}$, 0.02, 0.75.
14. 0.05, $\frac{1}{5}$, 0.045, $\frac{11}{12}$, 3, 0.5, $\frac{3}{5}$.
15. The heights in cm of seven children were
151, 160, 148, 143, 127, 159 and 133.
What is the median height?
16. A die was thrown ten times and the results
are shown below.

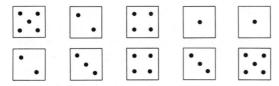

Find the median score
17. Each day a headmaster expels a certain
number of pupils for misbehaviour. During
one week the number of expulsions was 3,
11, 2, 1, 5. What was the median number of
expulsions?
18. In a really hard question a teacher asked a
class to find the median of the numbers
7, 1, 7, 1, 12, 8, 13, 3, 12, 4, 4, 11, 14, 25,
20, 19, 20, 18, 15.
What was the answer?

Exercise 4

In questions **1** to **6** find the mode.
1. 2, 3, 4, 2, 3, 4, 2, 5, 3, 2, 5.
2. 1, 3, 2, 3, 1, 3, 2, 2, 1, 3, 2, 3.
3. 3, 5, 6, 3, 5, 3, 4, 5, 6, 4, 6, 6.
4. 3, 7, 4, 1, 7, 4, 3, 8, 1, 7, 8.
5. 5, 7, 5, 6, 7, 6, 5, 6, 5, 6, 5, 6, 7, 7, 7, 7.
6. 5, 3, 4, 5, 6, 3, 5, 4, 3, 6, 4, 5, 6.
7. In various shops a tin of beans was priced in
pence as follows.
18, 19, 18, 19, 21, 18, 21, 23, 18, 23, 23.
What is the modal price?
8. The temperature in °C on 17 days was:
1, 0, 2, 2, 0, 4, 1, 3, 2, 1, 2, 3, 4, 5, 4, 5, 5.
What was the modal temperature?
9. A die was thrown 14 times as follows:

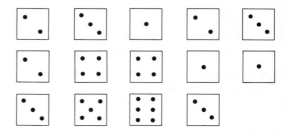

What was the modal score?
10. The bar chart shows the marks scored in a
test. What was the modal mark?

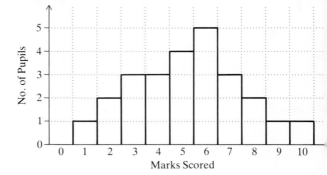

Exercise 5

Find (a) the mean, (b) the median, (c) the mode.
Begin each question by writing out the numbers in order of size.

1. 4, 2, 9, 5, 2.
2. 8, 3, 1, 8, 6, 1, 8.
3. 3, 4, 3, 5, 3, 4, 3, 4.
4. 1.2, 1.8, 0.1, 1.8, 0.6.
5. 17, 18, 18, 17, 18.
6. 4, 7, 8, 3, 4, 11, 8, 4, 4, 8.
7. 0.5, 0.5, 1.05, 0.05, 0.15.
8. 2, 1, 3, 2, 4, 1, 3, 4, 1, 2, 3, 3, 5, 4, 5, 5.
9. $\frac{1}{4}, \frac{3}{4}, \frac{1}{2}, \frac{3}{4}, \frac{1}{4}, \frac{1}{2}, 1\frac{3}{4}, \frac{1}{4}$.
10. $-1, -1, 2, -5, 4, -1, 2$.

11. 0.8, 0.68, 0.85, 0.85, 0.72.
12. $0, -1, 7, 3, -1, -3, 2$.
13. 4, 9, 1, 7, 19, 2, 5, 4, 11, 4, 11.
14. 13, 8, 11, 5, 13, 17, 21, 13, 2, 9, 9.
15. 102, 135, 117, 101, 101.
16. 1, 10, 5, 1, 9, 8, 1, 9, 1, 5, 5.
17. 0.111, 0.1, 0.111, 0.11, 0.01.
18. 0.32, 0.3, 0.302, 0.322, 0.322.
19. $-2, 2, -2, -3, 7, 4, -3, 4, -2, 5$.
20. 41, 47, 31, 41, 35, 39.

Calculating the mean from a frequency table

The frequency table shows the weights of the eggs bought in a supermarket.

weight	58 g	59 g	60 g	61 g	62 g	63 g
frequency	3	7	11	9	8	2

mean weight of eggs

$$= \frac{(58\times3) + (59\times7) + (60\times11) + (61\times9) + (62\times8) + (63\times2)}{(3 + 7 + 11 + 9 + 8 + 2)}$$

$$= \frac{2418}{40} = 60.45 \text{ g}$$

Exercise 6

1. The frequency table shows the weights of the 40 apples sold in a shop.

weight	70 g	80 g	90 g	100 g	110 g	120 g
frequency	2	7	9	11	8	3

Calculate the mean weight of the apples.

2. The frequency table shows the price of a packet of butter in 30 different shops.

price	49p	50p	51p	52p	53p	54p
frequency	2	3	5	10	6	4

Calculate the mean price of a packet of butter.

3. A box contains 50 nails of different lengths as shown in the frequency table.

length of nail	2 cm	3 cm	4 cm	5 cm	6 cm	7 cm
frequency	4	7	9	12	10	8

Calculate the mean length of the nails.

4. Thirty pupils in a class were asked to estimate the length of a straight line.
Their estimates are given in the frequency table.

estimated length	5 cm	6 cm	7 cm	8 cm	9 cm	10 cm
frequency	4	6	10	5	3	2

Calculate the mean of the estimates.

5. The numbers of eggs in 100 birds' nests are as follows:

number of eggs	1	2	3	4	5	6
frequency	5	15	25	30	15	10

Calculate the mean number of eggs per nest.

6. A group of 50 pupils took a test and their marks were as follows:

marks	5	6	7	8	9	10
frequency	3	8	9	13	9	8

Calculate the mean mark.

7. Twenty-five children were measured and their heights are recorded in the frequency table.

height	1.40 m	1.44 m	1.48 m	1.52 m	1.56 m
frequency	3	5	6	8	3

Calculate the mean height of the 25 children.

8. A class of children were timed when they each ran the length of the playground.

time	6 s	7 s	8 s	9 s	10 s	11 s
frequency	1	4	5	10	7	3

Calculate the mean time for the run.

7.2 CHARTS AND GRAPHS

Pie charts

The pie chart shows the holiday intentions of 600 people.

(a) Number of people camping $= \frac{60}{360} \times 600$
$= 100.$

(b) Number of people touring $= \frac{72}{360} \times 600$
$= 120.$

(c) Number of people at seaside $= \frac{102}{360} \times 600$
$= 170.$

Exercise 7

Draw the pie chart and then answer the questions.

1. The total cost of a holiday was £420. The pie chart shows how this cost was made up.

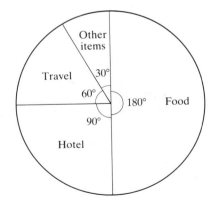

(a) How much was spent on food?
(b) How much was spent on travel?
(c) How much was spent on the hotel?
(d) How much was spent on other items?

2. Mr Billingsgate had an income of £6000. The pie chart shows how he used the money.

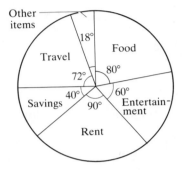

How much did he spend on
(a) Food,
(b) Rent,
(c) Savings,
(d) Entertainment,
(e) Travel?

3. The total expenditure of a County Council is £36 000 000. The pie chart shows how the money was spent.

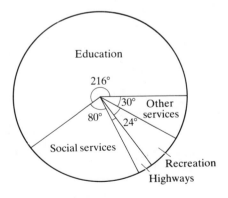

(a) How much was spent on
   (i) Education   (ii) Social services?
(b) What is the angle representing expenditure on highways?
(c) How much was spent on highways?

4. A firm employs 720 people in six departments as shown below.

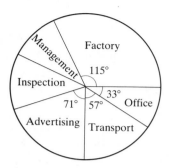

Copy and complete the table below.

Department	Angle on pie chart	Number employed
Factory	115°	
Office	33°	
Transport	57°	
Advertising	71°	
Inspection		140
Management		28

5. The pie chart shows how a pupil spends her time in a maths lesson which lasts 60 minutes.

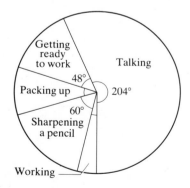

(a) How much time does she spend:
   (i) Getting ready to work;
   (ii) Talking;
   (iii) Sharpening a pencil?
(b) She takes 5 minutes to pack up. What is the corresponding angle on the pie chart?
(c) She spends 3 minutes working. What is the angle on the pie chart for the time spent working?

6. The pie chart below shows the breakdown of cost of an LP having a retail price of £4.99.

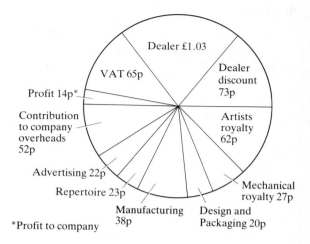

*Profit to company

(a) How much does the artist receive if 100 000 records are sold?
(b) How much VAT is paid on a record which sells one million copies?
(c) What are the manufacturing costs for producing 10 000 records?
(d) What is the profit to the company if 500 000 records are sold?

Exercise 8

1. At the semi-final stage of the F.A. Cup 72 neutral referees were asked to predict who they thought would win. Their answers were:

    Spurs   9
    Manchester United 40
    Everton   22
    York City   1

(a) Work out
   (i) $\frac{9}{72}$ of 360°   (ii) $\frac{40}{72}$ of 360°
   (iii) $\frac{22}{72}$ of 360°   (iv) $\frac{1}{72}$ of 360°
(b) Draw an accurate pie chart to display the predictions of the 72 referees.

2. A survey was carried out to find what 400
pupils did at the end of the fifth year:

       120 went into the sixth form
       160 went into employment
        80 went to F.E. colleges
        40 were unemployed.

(a) Simplify the following fractions:
$\frac{120}{400}, \frac{160}{400}, \frac{80}{400}, \frac{40}{400}.$

(b) Draw an accurate pie chart to show the
information above.

3. In a survey on washing powder 180 people
were asked to state which Brand they
preferred. 45 chose Brand A.

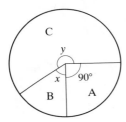

If 30 people chose Brand B and 105 chose
Brand C, calculate the angles x and y.

4. A packet of breakfast cereal weighing 600 g
contains four ingredients as follows:

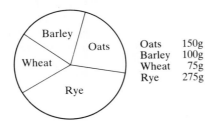

Oats	150g
Barley	100g
Wheat	75g
Rye	275g

Calculate the angles on the pie chart shown
and draw an accurate diagram.

5. The table below shows the share of British
car sales achieved by four companies in one
year.

Company	A	B	C	D
Share of sales	50%	10%	25%	15%

In a pie chart to show this information, find
the angle of the sectors r`presenting

(a) Company A   (b) Company B
(c) Company C   (d) Company D.

6. The teachers and pupils in a school were
asked to state which T.V. channel they
preferred. The results were

    BBC1   35%
    BBC2   5%
    ITV   50%
    Channel 4 10%

In a pie chart to show this information, find
the angle of the sectors representing the four
channels in the above order.

7. A pop singer's budget over a three month
period was as follows:

Recording latest single	£ 6000
Pressing record and producing sleeve	£ 3000
Poster campaign	£ 5000
Living expenses	£ 2000
Wardrobe	£ 2000
Total	£18000

Draw an accurate pie chart to show the
breakdown of his budget.

8. Calculate the angles on a pie chart
corresponding to items A, B, C, D and E
given in the tables.

(a)

item	A	B	C	D	E
number	5	2	3	6	2

(b)

item	A	B	C	D	E
length (m)	8	3	10	5	10

(c)

item	A	B	C	D	E
mass (g)	15	7	12	16	10

(d)

item	A	B	C	D	E
time (s)	40	7	9	5	11

(e)

item	A	B	C	D	E
number	250	40	100	80	130

Histograms, tally charts and bar charts

A histogram is a diagram which is used to represent a frequency distribution. It consists of a set of rectangles whose *areas* represent the frequency of the various data. If all the rectangles have the same width the frequencies will be represented by the heights of the rectangles.

Example

The tally chart shows the marks obtained by 36 pupils in a test.

Mark	Tally	Frequency
0	IIII	4
1	⊞I	6
2	IIII	4
3	⊞ ⊞ II	12
4	⊞ III	8
5	II	2

The same information is shown on a histogram.

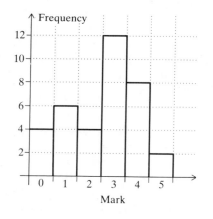

Mark

Exercise 9

1. The bar chart shows the sales figures for a firm over a number of years.

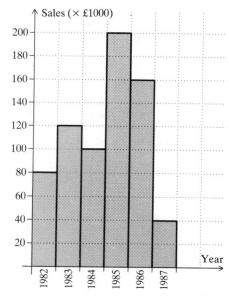

(a) What was the value of sales in 1983?
(b) In what year was the value of sales £160 000?
(c) In what year was the value of sales double the previous year's value?
(d) In 1983 the sales target was £90 000. By how much did the firm exceed its target?
(e) Write the total value of sales over 6 years.

2. The sales of records and cassettes is shown for the years 1980 and 1983.

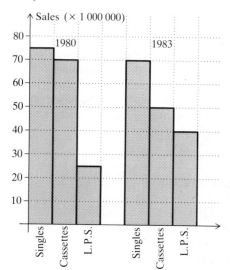

(a) What were the sales of cassettes in 1980?
(b) What were the sales of LP's in 1983?
(c) What was the drop in sales of cassettes between 1980 and 1983?
(d) What was the increase in sales of LP's between 1980 and 1983?
(e) The average price of a single in 1983 was £1.20. How much money was spent on singles in 1983?

3. In a survey the number of occupants in the cars passing a school was recorded.

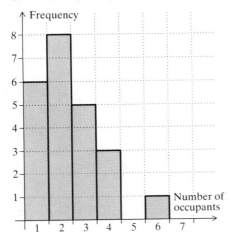

(a) How many cars had 3 occupants?
(b) How many cars had less than 4 occupants?
(c) How many cars were in the survey?
(d) What was the total number of occupants in all the cars in the survey?
(e) What fraction of the cars had only one occupant?

4. The seven best-selling cars in 1984 were:

    1. Escort   157 340
    2. Cavalier 132 049
    3. Fiesta   126 311
    4. Metro   117 442
    5. Sierra   113 071
    6. Maestro   83 072
    7. Astra   56 511

(a) Round off the above figures to the nearest 10 000.
(b) Draw a bar chart to illustrate the sales of the cars using the figures obtained in part (a).

5. The bar chart shows the profit/loss figures for a shop.

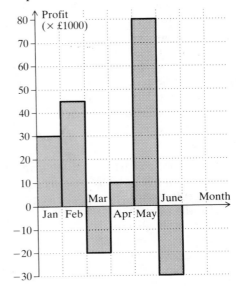

(a) What was the profit in February?
(b) What was the loss in June?
(c) In how many months did the shop make a profit of more than £20 000?
(d) In which two consecutive months did the shop have its best performance?
(e) What was the overall profit for the first six months after the losses were subtracted?

6. In an experiment two dice were thrown sixty times and the total score showing was recorded.

2	3	5	4	8	6	4	7	5	10
7	8	7	6	12	11	8	11	7	6
6	5	7	7	8	6	7	3	6	7
12	3	10	4	3	7	2	11	8	5
7	10	7	5	7	5	10	11	7	10
4	8	6	4	6	11	6	12	11	5

(a) Draw a tally chart to show the results of the experiment. The tally chart is started below.

Score	Tally marks	Frequency
2	II	2
3	IIII	4
4		
:		

(b) Draw a histogram to illustrate the results. Plot the frequency on the vertical axis.

7. In a survey of the cars in a car park the letter
    at the beginning or the end of the registration
    number was recorded. Eighty letters were
    recorded as follows:

D	P	R	B	D	C	D	R	S	A
P	R	T	P	T	B	W	P	T	V
V	B	N	R	W	A	A	N	V	X
T	V	A	C	X	X	T	B	W	W
A	T	C	T	B	A	X	W	X	T
N	D	V	S	S	V	V	C	T	R
V	W	W	V	T	T	R	X	C	S
W	X	X	X	W	S	D	T	D	B

    (a) Draw a tally chart so that you can count
         up the number of cars bearing a
         particular letter.
    (b) Use the tally chart to answer the
         following questions:
         (i) How many cars had an 'X'
              registration?
         (ii) What registration letter was most
              common?

8. In a survey the passengers on an aircraft were
    asked to state their age in years. The replies
    are shown below:

29	57	21	41	31	13	43	39	18	5
7	30	28	5	22	38	37	29	47	63
33	25	45	36	35	23	49	5	36	55
10	34	32	15	42	26	32	48	27	68

    (a) Draw a tally chart for ages 0–9, 10–19,
         20–29 etc.
    (b) Draw a histogram to illustrate the results.
         Plot frequency on the vertical axis.
    (c) How many passengers were in the age
         range 30–39?

Line graphs

Exercise 10

1. Which of the graphs A to D below best fits the following statement:
    'Unemployment is still rising but by less each month.'

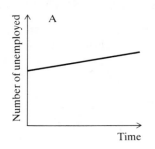 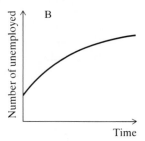 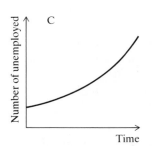 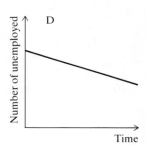

2. Which of the graphs A to D best fits the following statement:
    'The price of oil was rising more rapidly in 1983 than at any time in the
    previous ten years.'

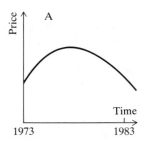 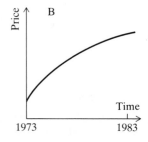 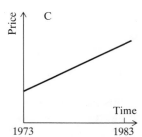 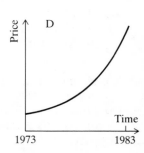

3. Which of the graphs A to D below best fits each of the following
   statements:
   (a) The birthrate was falling but is now steady.
   (b) Unemployment, which rose slowly until 1980, is now rising rapidly.
   (c) Inflation, which has been rising steadily, is now beginning to fall.
   (d) The price of gold has fallen steadily over the last year.

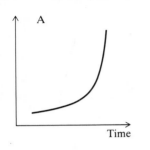 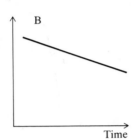 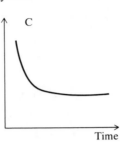 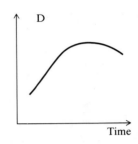

4. The length of a spring is measured with various loads suspended from
   the spring. The results are shown below.

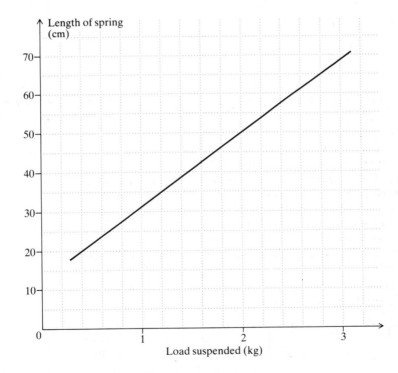

   (a) What is the length of the spring with a load of
       (i) 1.2 kg   (ii) 2.4 kg   (iii) 1.6 kg?
   (b) What is the load when the length of the spring is
       (i) 50 cm   (ii) 65 cm   (iii) 35 cm?
   (c) By how much is the length of the spring increased when an extra 1
       kg is added to a load of 2 kg?
   (d) Estimate the length of the spring with no load.

5. The temperature in a centrally-heated home was recorded every hour for 24 hours. The results are shown below.

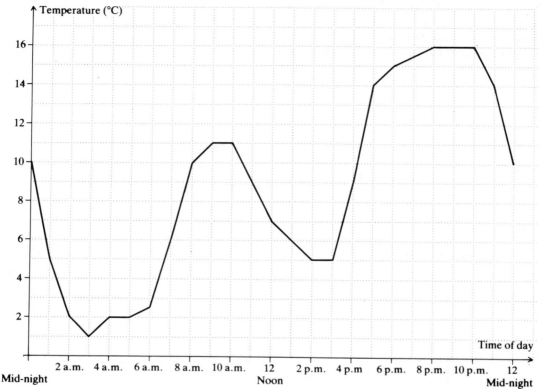

(a) What was the temperature at
   (i) 8 a.m.   (ii) 8 p.m.   (iii) 7 p.m.?
(b) At what two times was the temperature 14°C?
(c) What was the lowest temperature recorded and when did it occur?
(d) The heating in the house was switched 'on' and then 'off' twice during the day. Estimate
   (i) the two times when it was switched 'on'
   (ii) the two times when it was switched 'off'.
(e) What was the greatest increase in temperature in one hour and when did this occur?

6. The following table gives the cost £C to a householder for the work of a plumber when he works for x hours on a job.

Time x (hours)	1.0	2.0	3.5	4.5	6.5
Cost C (£)	10.50	16.50	25.50	31.50	43.50

(a) Draw a pair of axes with the horizontal scale for x from 0 to 7 and the vertical scale for C from 0 to 50.
(b) Plot the points given in the table and draw a straight line through the points.
(c) Use your graph to find
   (i) the cost to the householder when the plumber is working for 5 hours
   (ii) the length of time he is working when the cost to the householder is £19.50.

7. (a) The graph below gives the charges made by Welwyn Motors for the hire of a van to travel various distances.

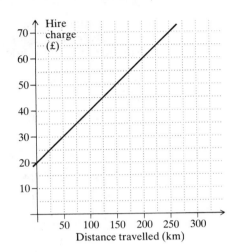

   (i) What is the hire charge for a van to travel 100 km?
   (ii) What was the distance travelled by a van for which the hire charge was £70?
(b) Cahill Motors also hire out vans. Their charges are shown below.

Distance travelled (km)	50	150	250
Hire charge (£)	45	55	65

   (i) Draw a copy of the graph above and on the same graph plot the points representing the hire charges for Cahill Motors. Draw a straight line through the points.
   (ii) For what distance do the two firms have the same hire charge?
   (iii) For a journey of 50 km, what is the difference in the hire charges made by these two firms?

8. The following table shows the petrol consumption of a car in litres per 100 km at different road speeds.

Road speed km/h	20	30	40	50	60	70	80	90	100
Consumption litres per 100 km	5.5	4.8	4.4	4	4	4.3	4.9	5.8	7.2

(a) Draw a pair of axes with road speed on the horizontal axis and petrol consumption on the vertical axis.
(b) Plot the nine points from the table and draw a smooth curve.
(c) From your graph estimate the most economical road speed for the car.
(d) Estimate the consumption in litres per 100 km at a speed of 95 km/h.
(e) If petrol costs 46p per litre, find the cost of a journey of 200 km if the car travels at a steady speed of 90 km/h.

7.3 PROBABILITY

If a 'trial' can have n equally likely outcomes and a 'success' can occur in s ways (from the n), then the probability of a 'success' $= \dfrac{s}{n}$.

A single card is drawn from a pack of 52 playing cards. Find the probability of the following results:
(a) the card is a Queen,
(b) the card is a Club,
(c) the card is the Jack of Hearts.

There are 52 equally likely outcomes of the 'trial' (drawing a card).
(a) p (Queen) $= \frac{4}{52} = \frac{1}{13}$
(b) p (Club) $= \frac{13}{52} = \frac{1}{4}$
(c) p (Jack of Hearts) $= \frac{1}{52}$.

Exercise 11

1. If one card is picked at random from a pack of 52 playing cards, what is the probability that it is:
    (a) a King,
    (b) the Ace of Clubs,
    (c) a Heart?

2. Nine counters numbered 1, 2, 3, 4, 5, 6, 7, 8, 9 are placed in a bag. One is taken out at random. What is the probability that it is:
    (a) a '5',
    (b) divisible by 3,
    (c) less than 5,
    (d) divisible by 4?

3. A bag contains 5 green balls, 2 red balls and 4 yellow balls. One ball is taken out at random. What is the probability that it is:
    (a) green,
    (b) red,
    (c) yellow?

4. A cash bag contains two 20p coins, four 10p coins, five 5p coins, three 2p coins and three 1p coins. Find the probability that one coin selected at random is:
    (a) a 10p coin,
    (b) a 2p coin,
    (c) a silver coin.

5. A bag contains 8 orange balls, 5 green balls and 4 silver balls. Find the probability that a ball picked out at random is:
    (a) silver,
    (b) orange,
    (c) green.

6. One card is selected at random from those below.

    Find the probability of selecting:
    (a) a Heart,
    (b) an Ace,
    (c) the 10 of Clubs,
    (d) a Spade,
    (e) a Heart or a Diamond.

7. A pack of playing cards is well shuffled and a card is drawn. Find the probability that the card is:
    (a) a Jack.
    (b) a Queen or a Jack,
    (c) the ten of Hearts,
    (d) a Club higher than the 9 (count the Ace as high).

8. The number of matches in ten boxes is as follows: 48, 46, 45, 49, 44, 46, 47, 48, 45, 46. One box is selected at random. Find the probability of the box containing:
    (a) 49 matches,
    (b) 46 matches,
    (c) more than 47 matches.

9. One ball is selected at random from those below.

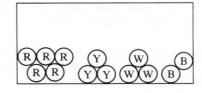

R = red
Y = yellow
W = white
B = black

Find the probability of selecting:
(a) a white ball,
(b) a yellow or a black ball,
(c) a ball which is not red.

10. (a) A bag contains 5 red balls, 6 green balls and 2 black balls. Find the probability of selecting:
    (i) a red ball   (ii) a green ball.
    (b) One black ball is removed from the bag. Find the new probability of selecting:
    (i) a red ball   (ii) a black ball.

11. A small pack of 20 cards consists of the Ace, King, Queen, Jack and ten of all four suits. Find the probability of selecting from this pack:
(a) an Ace,
(b) the Queen of Spades,
(c) a red card,
(d) any King or Queen.

12. A bag contains 12 white balls, 12 green balls and 12 purple balls. After 3 white balls, 4 green balls and 9 purple balls have been removed, what is the probability that the next ball to be selected will be white?

Exercise 12

1. The King of Hearts is drawn from a pack and not replaced. Find the probability that the next card is:
(a) another King,
(b) another Heart,
(c) the Ace of Hearts,
(d) the seven of Diamonds.

2. The Ace, King and Queen of Diamonds are drawn from a pack and not replaced. Find the probability that the next card is:
(a) another Ace,
(b) another Diamond,
(c) the Ace of Spades,
(d) the Queen of Hearts.

3. (a) A bag contains 5 blue discs, 4 orange discs and 2 white discs. What is the probability of picking out:
   (i) a blue disc,
   (ii) either a white or an orange disc,
   (iii) either a blue or a white disc,
   (iv) a disc which is not white?

(b) Two of the orange discs are now removed and are replaced by one blue disc and one white disc. What is the new probability of picking out:
   (i) a blue disc,
   (ii) an orange disc,
   (iii) either a white or an orange disc?

4. The 36 possible results, when throwing a red die and a blue die, are shown below. For example the point marked with a cross represents a '6' on the blue die and a '3' on the red die.

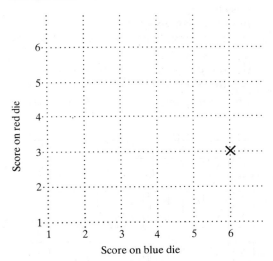

Calculate the probability of scoring in one throw of the two dice:
(a) a total of 12,
(b) a total of 9,
(c) a total of 2,
(d) a double (ie same score on both dice),
(e) a total of more than 9,
(f) a double *and* a total of 10.

5. A boy has 3 coins (5p, 2p and 1p) and he spins all three. Copy and complete the table below to show *all* the possible ways in which they could land. You will need to draw more columns than those shown.

5p	H			
2p	H			
1p	H			

Find the probability of obtaining:
(a) three tails,
(b) two heads and a tail (in any order),
(c) one head and two tails.

6. A girl has 4 coins (50p, 10p, 5p, 2p) and she spins all four. Draw a table to show all the possible ways in which they could land.
Find the probability of obtaining:
(a) four heads,
(b) three heads and a tail (in any order),
(c) two heads and two tails (in any order),
(d) one head and three tails (in any order).

7. Four balls are placed in a bag, 1 red, 1 blue, 1 green and 1 white. Two balls at random are withdrawn in one hand from the bag. List all the different colour combinations which are possible.
Find the probability that:
(a) the red ball and the green ball will be withdrawn,
(b) the blue ball will be withdrawn,
(c) the white ball will be left in the bag.

8. The numbering on a set of 28 dominoes is as follows:

6	6	6	6	6	6	6		5	5	5
6	5	4	3	2	1	0		5	4	3

5	5	5		4	4	4	4	4		3	3
2	1	0		4	3	2	1	0		3	2

3	3		2	2	2		1	1		0
1	0		2	1	0		1	0		0

(a) What is the probability of drawing a domino from a full set with
  (i) at least one six on it?
  (ii) at least one four on it?
  (iii) at least one two on it?
(b) What is the probability of drawing a 'double' from a full set?
(c) If I draw a double five which I do not return to the set, what is the probability of drawing another domino with a five on it?

Tree diagrams

A bag contains 5 yellow balls and 4 green balls. A ball is drawn at random and then replaced. Another ball is drawn. Find the probability of drawing:
(a) two yellow balls,
(b) one ball of each colour.

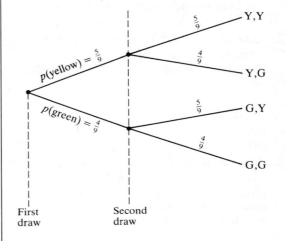

First draw   Second draw

(a) p (two yellow balls) $= \frac{5}{9} \times \frac{5}{9} = \frac{25}{81}$

(b) p (one of each colour)

$$= (\tfrac{5}{9} \times \tfrac{4}{9}) + (\tfrac{4}{9} \times \tfrac{5}{9})$$

$$= \tfrac{20}{81} + \tfrac{20}{81}$$

$$= \tfrac{40}{81}$$

Exercise 13

1. A bag contains 5 green balls and 3 white balls. A ball is drawn at random and then replaced. A second ball is then drawn. Copy and complete the tree diagram below.

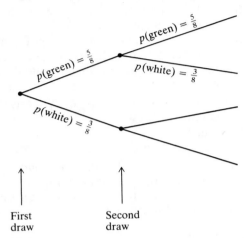

First draw   Second draw

Find the probability of the following:
(a) both balls are green,
(b) both balls are white.

2. A bag contains 3 red balls and 4 yellow balls. A ball is drawn at random and then replaced. A second ball is drawn. Draw a tree diagram to show all the possible outcomes. Find the probability of the following:
(a) both balls are red,
(b) both balls are yellow,
(c) the first ball is red and the second is yellow.

3. A bag contains 4 white balls, 2 black balls and 1 pink ball. A ball is drawn and then replaced. A second ball is drawn. Find the probability of the following:
(a) both balls are pink,
(b) both balls are white,
(c) the first ball is white and the second is black,
(d) the two balls are pink and white in any order.

4. A bag contains 5 red balls and 3 blue balls. A ball is drawn and *not* replaced. A second ball is drawn.
(a) Copy and complete the tree diagram.

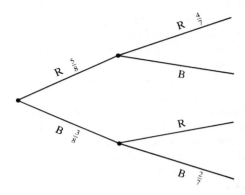

(b) Find the probability of drawing:
 (i) two red balls,
 (ii) two blue balls.

5. A bag contains 2 orange discs and 5 green discs. A disc is drawn and not replaced. A second disc is drawn. Find the probability of drawing:
(a) two orange discs,
(b) two green discs,
(c) an orange disc and a green disc in that order.

6. A ball is drawn from the box below and not replaced. A second ball is drawn.

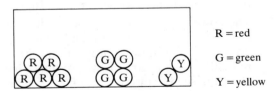

R = red
G = green
Y = yellow

Find the probability of drawing:
(a) two red balls,
(b) two yellow balls,
(c) a red ball and a green ball in that order,
(d) a green ball and a yellow ball in any order.

7. A bag contains 2 white balls and 3 black balls. A ball is drawn and then replaced. A second ball is drawn and then replaced. A third ball is drawn. Find the probability of drawing:
   (a) three white balls,
   (b) three black balls,
   (c) one black ball and two white balls in that order.

8. A card is drawn from a pack of 52 playing cards and is then replaced. Two further draws are made, again without replacement. Draw a tree diagram showing at each branch the two events 'spade' and 'not spade'. What is the probability of drawing:
   (a) three spades,
   (b) no spades,
   (c) one spade and two other suits in any order?

9. An ordinary die is thrown three times. Draw a tree diagram, showing at each branch the two events 'six' and 'not six'. What is the probability of throwing:
   (a) three sixes,
   (b) no sixes.

10. A fair coin is tossed three times. Draw a tree diagram, showing at each branch the two events 'head' and 'tail'. What is the probability of throwing:
    (a) three heads,
    (b) no heads,
    (c) one head and two tails in any order?

11. The flower seeds in a packet look identical but, in fact, give three differently coloured flowers in the following proportions: 50% red; 30% yellow; 20% white. Assume that all of the seeds will grow into flowers when planted.
    (a) What is the probability that a flower will be white?
    (b) What is the probability that a flower will not be yellow?
    (c) Draw a tree diagram for the colour of the flowers of the first two seeds.
    (d) What is the probability that the first two flowers will be:
       (i) both red;
       (ii) a red and a yellow in any order;
       (iii) both white?

12. There are red, white and yellow discs in a bag. The probability of picking a red disc is $\frac{1}{9}$, and the probability of picking a white disc is $\frac{4}{9}$. Find the probability of picking:
    (a) a yellow disc,
    (b) either a red or a white disc.
    (c) If there are 36 discs altogether in the bag, how many are white?
    (d) If a disc is picked from the bag, replaced and then a second disc is picked, what is the probability of picking a white disc both times?

13. A fair coin is tossed four times. What is the probability of throwing:
    (a) four heads,
    (b) two heads and two tails in any order?

14. A coin is biassed so that the probability of a 'head' is $\frac{2}{3}$ and the probability of a 'tail' is $\frac{1}{3}$. The coin is tossed three times. What is the probability of throwing:
    (a) three 'tails',
    (b) one 'head' and two 'tails' in any order?

15. From a pack of playing cards all the Jacks, Queens and Kings are removed. This leaves the Ace, 2, 3, 4, 5, 6, 7, 8, 9 and 10 of the four suits Spades, Hearts, Diamonds and Clubs; 40 cards in all.
    (a) one card is taken from these 40 cards. Find the probability that it is:
       (i) a '10',   (ii) a Spade,
       (iii) the Ace of Clubs,
       (iv) the seven of Hearts.
    (b) The 40 cards are turned over one by one. The first card turned over is the 8 of Clubs. What is the probability that the next card turned over is the 6 of Spades?
    (c) The 40 cards are now shuffled. They are turned over one by one. What is the probability that the first card turned over is the 5 of Diamonds *and* the second card turned over is the 4 of Hearts.

Part 8

8.1 ANGLES

Basic results

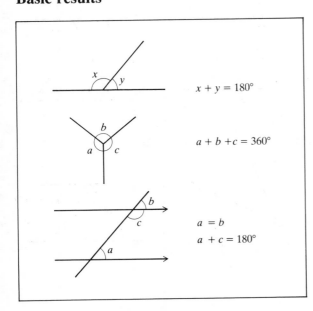

$x + y = 180°$

$a + b + c = 360°$

$a = b$
$a + c = 180°$

Exercise 1

Find the angles marked with letters. AB and CD are straight lines.

1.

132° x

A   B

2.

A

46°

y

B

3.

102° x
       x

A   B

4.

a
a 50°

A   B

5.

A   x   87°   B
x   x

6.

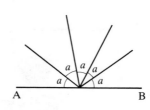

A
x
92°
x
B

7.

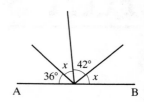

a   a   a
a   a
A   B

8.

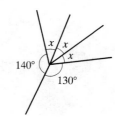

x   42°
36°   x
A   B

9.

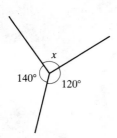

x
140°   120°

10.

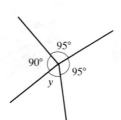

95°
90°   95°
y

11.

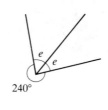

e
e
240°

12.

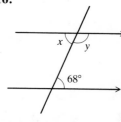

x   x
x
140°   130°

13.

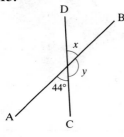

D   B
x
y
44°
A   C

14.

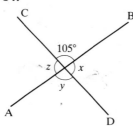

C   B
105°
z   x
y
A   D

15.

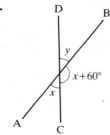

D   B
y
x + 60°
x
A   C

16.

x   y
68°

17.

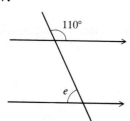

110°

e

18.

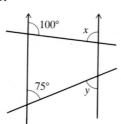

100°   x
75°   y

19.

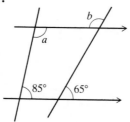

b
a
85°   65°

20.

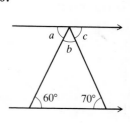

a   c
b
60°   70°

21.

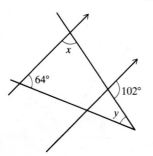

x
64°
102°
y

22.

2x
x

23.

y
3y

24.

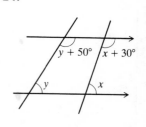

y + 50°   x + 30°
y   x

Triangles, quadrilaterals and regular polygons

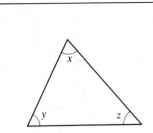 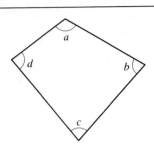 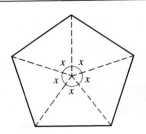

Triangle:
$x + y + z = 180°$

Quadrilateral:
$a + b + c + d = 360°$

Regular pentagon:
$x + x + x + x + x = 360°$
$\therefore x = 72°$

Exercise 2

Find the angles marked with letters.

1.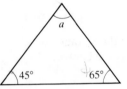

2.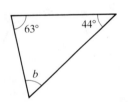

3.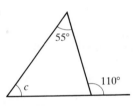

4.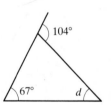

5.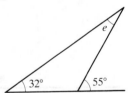

6.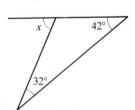

7.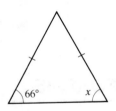

8.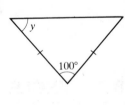

9.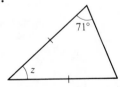

10.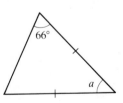

11.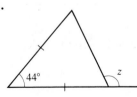

12.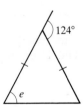

13.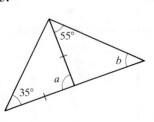

14.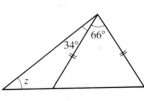

15.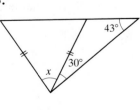

16.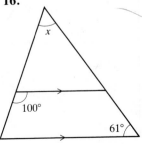

17.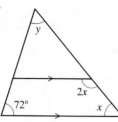

18.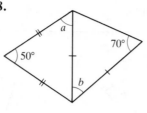

19.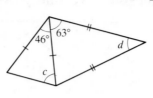

20.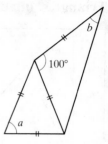

21.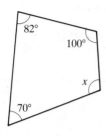

22.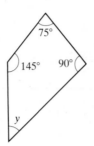

23.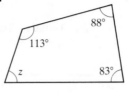

24.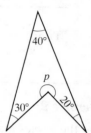

25.

regular hexagon
O is the centre.

26.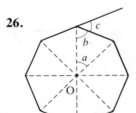

regular octagon
O is the centre.

8.2   CIRCLE THEOREMS

Theorem 1
The angle in a semicircle is a right angle

(a)

AOB is a diameter.

$a = 90°$
$b = 55°$

(b)

$\hat{ACB} = 90°$

$\therefore x + 3x = 90°$

[angle sum of a triangle]

$4x = 90°$
$x = 22\frac{1}{2}°$

Exercise 3

Draw each diagram and find the angles marked with letters. The line AOB
is a diameter.

1.

2.

3.

4.

5.

6.

7.

8.

9.

10.

11.

Find (a) XÂB
     (b) YB̂A
     (c) AX̂B

Tangent to a circle

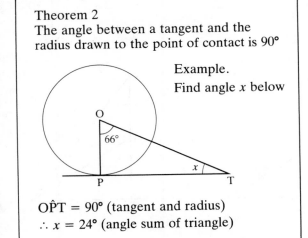

Theorem 2
The angle between a tangent and the
radius drawn to the point of contact is 90°

Example.
Find angle *x* below

OP̂T = 90° (tangent and radius)
∴ *x* = 24° (angle sum of triangle)

Exercise 4

Find the angles marked with letters. The point
O is the centre of the circle and TP is a tangent.

1.

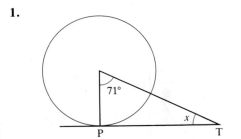

2.

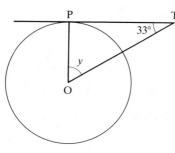

3.

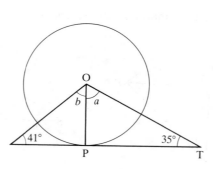

4.

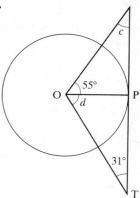

5.

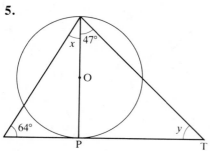

6.

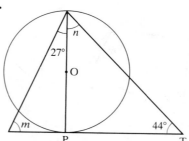

7.

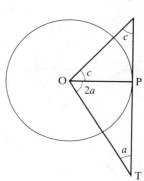

8.

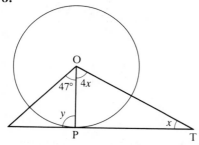

9.

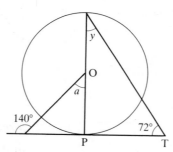

10.

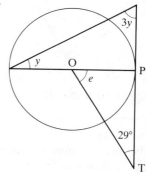

11.

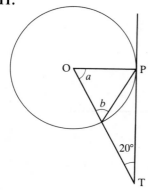

12.

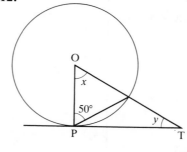

13.

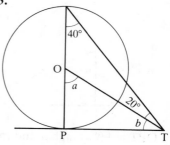

Theorem 3
Two tangents to a
circle are equal.

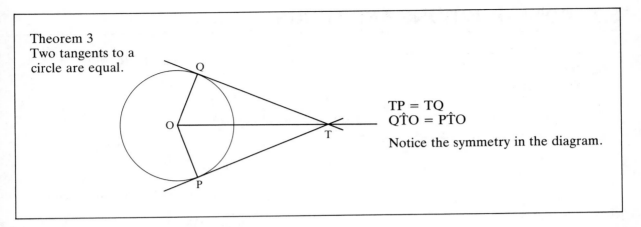

$TP = TQ$
$Q\hat{T}O = P\hat{T}O$

Notice the symmetry in the diagram.

Exercise 5

Find the angles marked with letters.

1.

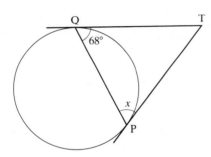

2.

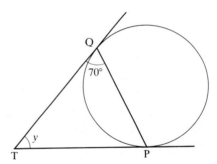

3.

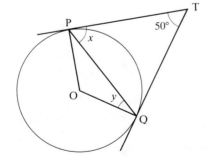

4.

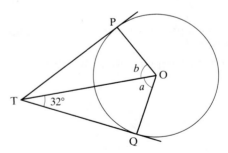

5.

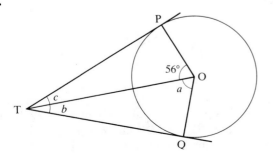

6.

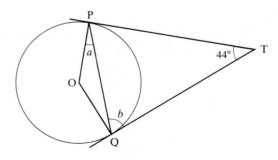

8.3 CONSTRUCTIONS AND LOCUS

(a) Perpendicular bisector of a line

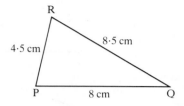

The broken line is the locus of a point which is equidistant from A and from B.

(b) Angle bisector.

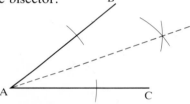

The broken line is the locus of a point which is equidistant from the lines AB and AC.

Exercise 6

You need a pair of compasses, a ruler and a sharp pencil.

1. (a) Construct triangle ABC (full size).

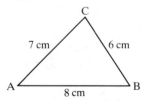

   (b) Construct the perpendicular bisector of AB. Measure the length MN.

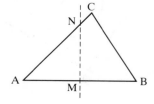

2. (a) Construct triangle PQR.

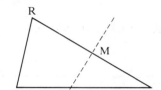

   (b) Construct the perpendicular bisector of RQ.
   Measure MN.

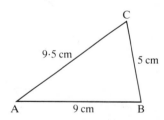

3. (a) Construct triangle ABC.

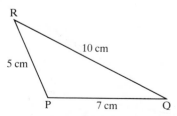

   (b) Construct the perpendicular bisectors of AB, AC and BC. They should meet in a single point O.
   (c) Draw a circle through A, B and C with centre O and radius OA. This is the *circumcircle* of triangle ABC.

4. (a) Construct triangle PQR.

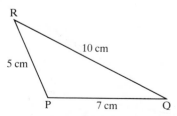

   (b) Construct the perpendicular bisectors of PQ, RQ and RP and hence draw the circumcircle of triangle PQR.

5. (a) Construct triangle ABC.

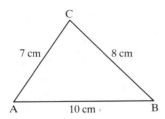

(b) Construct the bisectors of angles A, B
and C. They should meet in a single point
O.

(c) Draw a circle, with centre O, which just
touches the three sides of the triangle.
This is the *inscribed* circle of triangle ABC.

6. (a) Construct triangle XYZ.

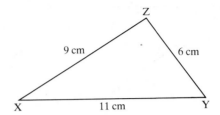

(b) Construct the bisectors of angles X, Y
and Z and hence construct the inscribed
circle of triangle XYZ.

8.4 TRIGONOMETRY

Finding angles

Find the angle x.

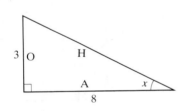

$\tan x = \dfrac{O}{A} = \dfrac{3}{8}$

$\tan x = 0.375$
$\quad x = 20.6°$ (to 1 D.P.)

Remember:

$\sin x = \dfrac{O}{H}; \quad \cos x = \dfrac{A}{H}; \quad \tan x = \dfrac{O}{A}$

Exercise 7

Find the angles marked with letters. All the lengths are in cm.

1.

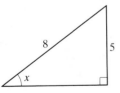

2.

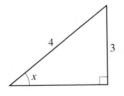

3.

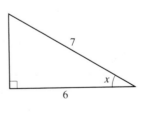

4.

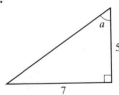

5.

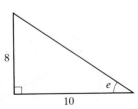

6.

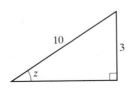

7.

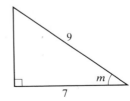

8.

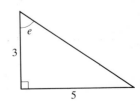

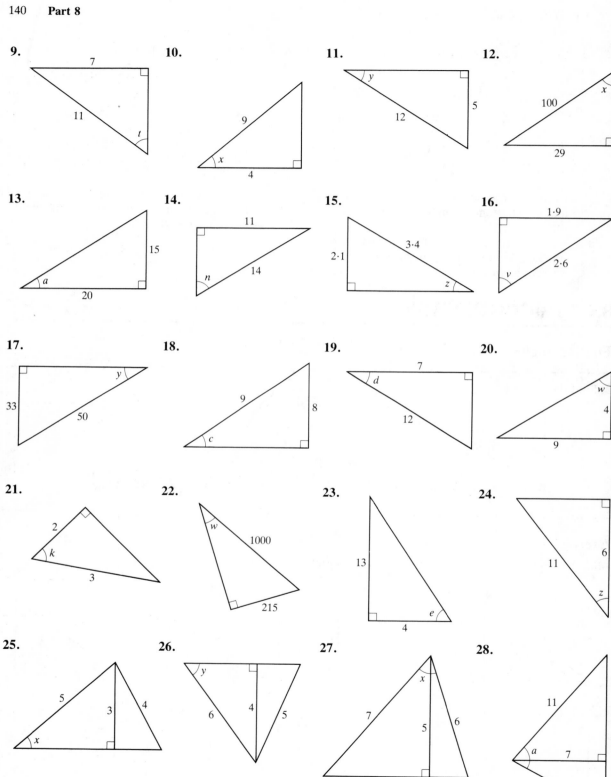

9.   7   11   *t*

10.   9   *x*   4

11.   *y*   12   5

12.   *x*   100   29

13.   15   *a*   20

14.   11   *n*   14

15.   3·4   2·1   *z*

16.   1·9   2·6   *v*

17.   *y*   33   50

18.   9   8   *c*

19.   7   *d*   12

20.   *w*   4   9

21.   2   *k*   3

22.   *w*   1000   215

23.   13   4   *e*

24.   6   11   *z*

25.   5   3   4   *x*

26.   *y*   6   4   5

27.   *x*   7   5   6

28.   11   *a*   7   9

Finding the length of a side

Find the length of *l*.

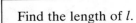

$$\cos 32° = \frac{A}{H} = \frac{l}{10}$$

$$\therefore l = 10 \times \cos 32°$$

$$l = 8.48 \text{ cm (to 3 s.f.)}$$

Exercise 8

Find the lengths marked with letters. All lengths are in cm. Give answers correct to 3 S.F.

1.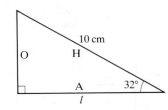

2.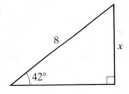

3.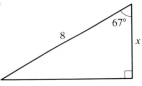

4.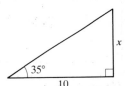

5.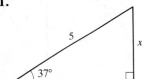

6.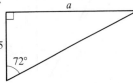

7.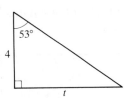

8.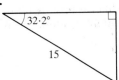

9.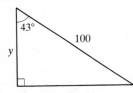

10.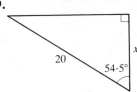

11.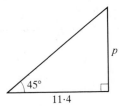

12.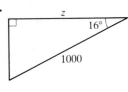

13.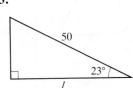

14.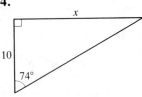

15.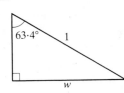

16.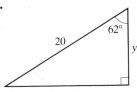

17.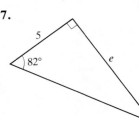

18.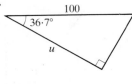

19.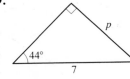

20.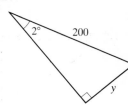

Find the length x.

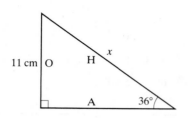

$$\sin 36° = \frac{O}{H} = \frac{11}{x}$$

$$\therefore x \sin 36° = 11$$

$$x = \frac{11}{\sin 36°} = 18.7 \text{ cm (to 3 s.f.)}$$

Exercise 9

This exercise is more difficult. Find the lengths and angles marked with letters.

1.

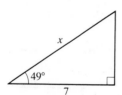

2.

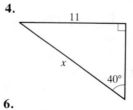

3.

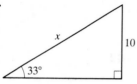

4.

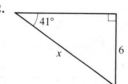

5.

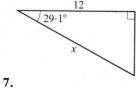

6.

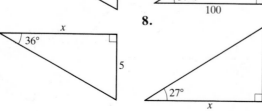

7.

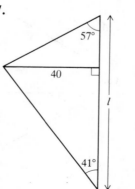

8.

9.

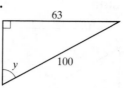

10.

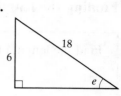

11.

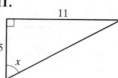

12.

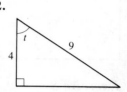

13.

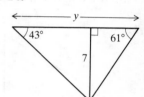

14.

15.

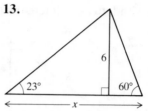

16.

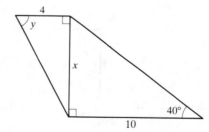

17.

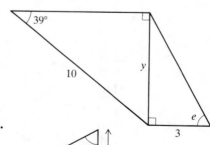

18.

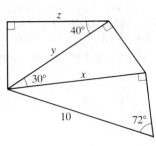

19.

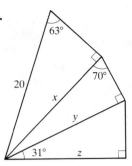

20.

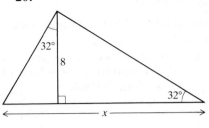

The next exercise is more difficult. It involves finding angles and sides using either trigonometry or Pythagoras' theorem.

Exercise 10

Find the angles and sides marked with letters. All lengths are in cm.

1.

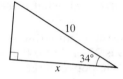

2.

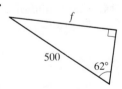

3.

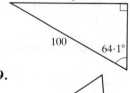

4.

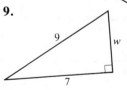

5.

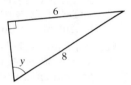

6.

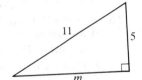

7.

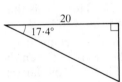

8.

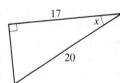

9.

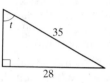

10.

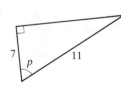

11.

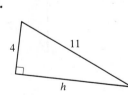

12.

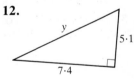

13.

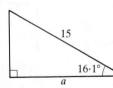

14.

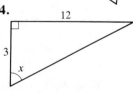

15.

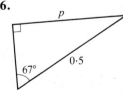

16.

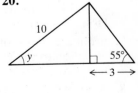

17.

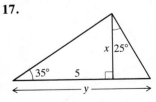

18.

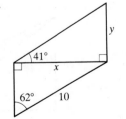

19.

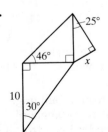

20.

Exercise 11

Begin each question by drawing a large clear diagram.

1. A ladder of length 4 m rests against a vertical wall so that the base of the ladder is 1.5 m from the wall.

    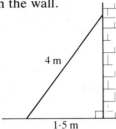

    Calculate the angle between the ladder and the ground.

2. A ladder of length 5 m rests against a vertical wall so that the base of the ladder is 3 m from the wall. Calculate the angle between the ladder and the ground.

3. A ladder of length 6 m rests against a vertical wall so that the angle between the ladder and the wall is 25°. How far is the base of the ladder from the wall?

4. A ladder of length 4 m rests against a vertical wall so that the angle between the ladder and the ground is 66°. How far up the wall does the ladder reach?

5. From a distance of 20 m the angle of elevation to the top of a tower is 35°.

    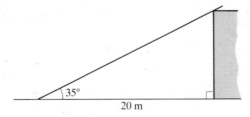

    How high is the tower?

6. From a distance of 100 m the angle of elevation to the top of a tall tree is 11.2°. How tall is the tree?

7. From a distance of 30 m, the angle of elevation to the top of a tower is 21.6°. How high is the tower?

8. A point G is 40 m away from a building, which is 15 m high. What is the angle of elevation to the top of the building from G?

9. A point X is 100 m away from a flagpole, which is 27 m high. What is the angle of elevation to the top of the flagpole from X?

10. A boy is flying a kite from a string of length 60 m.

    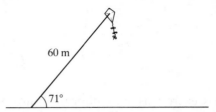

    If the string is taut and makes an angle of 71° with the horizontal, what is the height of the kite? Ignore the height of the boy.

11. A girl is flying a kite from a string of length 50 m. If the string is taut and makes an angle of 36° with the horizontal, what is the height of the kite?

12. A man is flying a kite from a taut string of length 40 m. If the kite is 22 m above the ground calculate the angle between the string and the ground.

13. A straight tunnel is 80 m long and slopes downwards at an angle of 11° to the horizontal. Find the vertical drop in travelling from the top to the bottom of the tunnel.

14. The frame of a bicycle is shown in the diagram.

    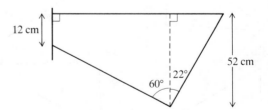

    Find the length of the cross bar.

15. Calculate the length *x*.

    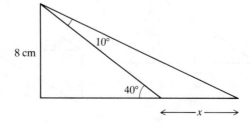

16. AB is a chord of a circle of radius 5 cm and centre O.

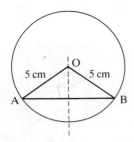

The perpendicular bisector of AB passes through O and also bisects the angle AOB. If AÔB = 100° calculate the length of the chord AB.

17. A chord XY of length 8 cm is drawn in a circle of radius 6 cm, centre O. Calculate the angle XOY.

18. A chord PQ of length 10 cm is drawn in a circle with centre O. If the angle POQ is 88° calculate the radius of the circle.

Exercise 12

1. A ship is due South of a lighthouse. It sails on a bearing of 055° for a distance of 80 km until it is due East of the lighthouse.

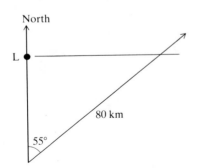

How far is it now from the lighthouse?

2. A ship is due South of a lighthouse. It sails on a bearing of 071° for a distance of 200 km until it is due East of the lighthouse. How far is it now from the lighthouse?

3. An aircraft is due North of a radio tower. It flies for a distance of 100 km on a bearing of 152° until it is due East of the tower. How far is it now from the tower?

4. An aircraft is due West of a control tower. It flies on a bearing of 040° at a speed of 300 km/h for two hours until it is due North of the tower. How far is it now from the tower?

5. A ship is due North of a lighthouse. It sails on a bearing of 200° at a speed of 15 km/h for five hours until it is due West of the lighthouse. How far is it now from the lighthouse?

6. A submarine is due South of an underwater port. It sails on a bearing of 300° for a distance of 160 km until it is due West of the port. How far is it now from the port?

7. Calculate the length *y*.

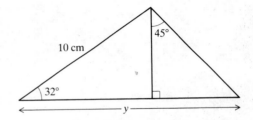

8. From a horizontal distance of 40 m, the angle of elevation to the top of a building is 35.4°. From a point further away from the building the angle of elevation is 20.2°. What is the distance between the two points?

Part 9

REVISION TESTS

Revision test 1

1. Cheese is on sale at £1.94 per kilogram. Mrs Jones bought half a kilogram and paid with a one pound coin. How much change did she receive?

2. Fifteen books weigh 3 kg altogether. How many grams does one book weigh?

3. A man buys 500 pencils at 2.4 pence each. What change does he receive from £20?

4. Every day at school Stephen buys a roll for 14p, crisps for 11p and a drink for 21p. How much does he spend in pounds in the whole school year of 200 days?

5. An athlete runs 25 laps of a track in 30 minutes 10 seconds.
   (a) How many seconds does he take to run 25 laps?
   (b) How long does he take to run one lap, if he runs the 25 laps at a constant speed?

6. A pile of 250 tiles is 2 m thick. What is the thickness of one tile in cm?

7. Work out
   (a) 20% of £65   (b) 37% of £400   (c) 8.5% of £2000.

8. In a text, the marks of nine pupils were 7, 5, 2, 7, 4, 9, 7, 6, 6. Find
   (a) the mean mark   (b) the median mark   (c) the modal mark.

9. Work out
   (a) $-6 - 5$ (b) $-7 + 30$ (c) $-13 + 3$
   (d) -4×5 (e) -3×-2 (f) $-4 + -10$

10. Given $a = 3$, $b = -2$ and $c = 5$, work out
   (a) $b + c$ (b) $a - b$ (c) ab (d) $a + bc$

11. Solve the equations
   (a) $x - 6 = 3$ (b) $x + 9 = 20$ (c) $x - 5 = -2$
   (d) $3x + 1 = 22$

12. Find the area of the shapes below.

(a)
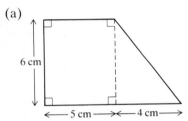

(b)
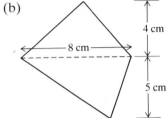

13. (a) Copy and complete the table of values for the graph of $y = 2x - 3$.

x	-2	-1	0	1	2	3	4
$2x$ -3							
y							

   (b) Draw the graph of $y = 2x - 3$.

14. (a) Draw a pair of axes for x and y from -7 to $+7$.
   (b) Plot and label A(1, 6), B(5, 6), C(5, 4).
   (c) Draw the image of $\triangle$ABC after the following rotations:
       (i) 90° clockwise about (2, 2). Label it A′B′C′.
       (ii) 180° about (1, 4). Label it A″B″C″.
       (iii) 90° anticlockwise about (4, −3). Label it A*B*C*.
   (d) Write down the coordinates of A′, A″ and A*.

15. (a) Draw a pair of axes for x and y from -7 to $+7$.
   (b) Plot and label P(1, 3), Q(1, 7), R(3, 7).
   (c) Draw the image of $\triangle$PQR after reflection in
       (i) the line $y = 1$. Label it P′Q′R′.
       (ii) the line $x = -1$. Label it P″Q″R″.
       (iii) the line $y = x$. Label it P*Q*R*.
   (d) Write down the coordinates of P′, P″ and P*.

Revision test 2

1. Solve the equations
   (a) $3x - 1 = 20$.
   (b) $4x + 3 = 4$.
   (c) $5x - 7 = -3$.

2. Copy the diagrams and then calculate x, correct to 3 s.f.
   (a)

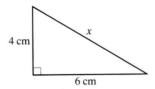

   (b)

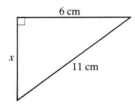

   (c)

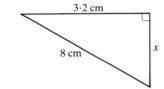

3. A bag contains 3 red balls and 5 white balls. Find the probability of selecting:
   (a) a red ball,
   (b) a white ball.

4. A box contains 2 yellow discs, 4 blue discs and 5 green discs. Find the probability of selecting:
   (a) a yellow disc,
   (b) a green disc,
   (c) a blue or a green disc.

5. Copy and complete the table, giving correct units.

	Speed	Distance	Time
(a)	10 m/s	200 m	
(b)		120 km	4 h
(c)	24 m.p.h.		30 minutes
(d)	240 km/h	20 km	

6. Work out on a calculator, correct to 4 s.f.
   (a) $3.61 - (1.6 \times 0.951)$
   (b) $\dfrac{(4.65 + 1.09)}{(3.6 - 1.714)}$

7. Find the area, correct to 3 s.f.

(a)

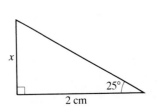

(b)

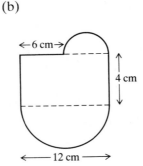

8. Draw the graph of $y = x^2 + 3x - 6$ for values of x from -4 to $+2$.

9. Plot the points given and join them up in order. Find the area of the shape enclosed.
(1, 2), (5, 7), (7,4), (5, 1), (1, 2).

10. Calculate the length x.

(a)   (b)

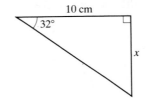

Revision test 3

Formulae: area of a circle $= \pi r^2$
circumference of a circle $= 2\pi r$
volume of cylinder $= \pi r^2 h$
volume of cone $= \frac{1}{3}\pi r^2 h$
volume of sphere $= \frac{4}{3}\pi r^3$

1. A shopkeeper sells 7 kg of potatoes for £1.26. Find
(a) the cost of 1 kg of potatoes
(b) how many kg of potatoes can be bought for £1.98.

2. Arrange the following numbers in order, smallest first.
(a) 3047, 3740, 3407, 3017
(b) 0.31, 0.13, 0.151, 0.301
(c) 0.75, 7.5, 0.075, 0.715
(d) 0.09, 0.089, 0.9, 0.0095

3. An aircraft's flight started at 21 40 on Tuesday and finished at 08 10 on the following Wednesday. How long was the journey in hours and minutes?

4. Copy and complete
   (a) 410 cm =   m
   (b) 63 m =   cm
   (c) 480 g =   kg
   (d) 2.2 km =   m
   (e) 0.07 m =   cm

5. Divide £80 in the ratio 1:3:4.

6. Work out, to the nearest penny
   (a) 40% of £65   (b) 22% of £16   (c) 7% of £12.40   (d) 11% of £7.63

7. In a sale all prices are reduced by 30%. Find the sale price of an article which normally costs £80.

8. Find the angles marked with letters.

(a) 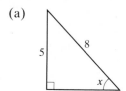 (b) 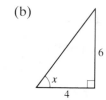 (c) 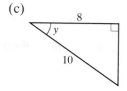 (d)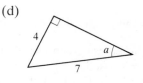

9. Find the volume of the following solid objects. Take π = 3.14 or use the 'π' button on a calculator. Give the answers to 3 s.f.

(a)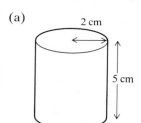

(b)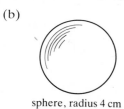

sphere, radius 4 cm

(c)

hemisphere, radius 5 cm

10. Solve the equations:
   (a) $5x + 1 = 26$
   (b) $3x - 1 = 1$
   (c) $4x + 1 = 2x + 9$
   (d) $7x - 3 = 2x + 12$

11. Write down each sequence and find the next two numbers.
   (a) 2, 9, 16, 23,
   (b) 20, 18, 16, 14,
   (c) −5, −2, 1, 4,
   (d) 128, 64, 32, 16,
   (e) 8, 11, 15, 20,

12. (a) Draw a pair of axes for x and y from −7 to +7.
   (b) Plot and label A(1, 3), B(1, 6), C(3, 6).
   (c) Draw the image of △ ABC after reflection in the following lines:
      (i) the y-axis. Label it △1.
      (ii) the x-axis. Label it △2.
      (iii) the line $y = 2$. Label it △3.
      (iv) the line $y = x$. Label it △4.
   (d) Write down the coordinates of the image of point A in each case.

EXAMINATION EXERCISES

Examination exercise 1

1. Copy the following bill and complete it by filling in the four blank spaces.

   8 rolls of wallpaper at £3.20 each   = £ ...
   3 tins of paint at £ ... each   = £ 20.10
   ... brushes at £2.40 each   = £ 9.60
               Total   = £ ...

   [M]

2. (a) The diagram represents a view of a cubical die. The number of dots on opposite faces adds up to seven. Write down the number of dots on the back face and on the bottom face as indicated in the diagram.

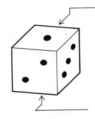

   (b) The diagram represents the net of another die. As before, the number of dots on opposite faces adds up to seven. Write down the numbers that would appear on the faces marked A, B and C respectively.

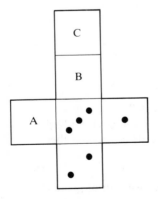

   [M]

3. A train travels between Watford and Coventry, a distance of 108 km, in 45 minutes, at a steady speed. It passes through Rugby 40 minutes after leaving Watford. How far, in km, is it from Rugby to Coventry?

   [L]

4. Look at the number pattern below.

$(2 \times 1) - 1 = 2 - 1$

$(3 \times 3) - 2 = 8 - 1$

$(4 \times 5) - 3 = 18 - 1$

$(5 \times 7) - 4 = 32 - 1$

$(6 \times a) - 5 = b - 1$

  (i) What number does the letter a stand for?

 (ii) What number does the letter b stand for?

(iii) Write down the next line in the pattern.

[N]

5. The faces of a round and a square clock are exactly the same area. If the round clock has a radius of 10 cm, how wide is the square clock?

 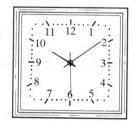

[S]

6. (i) The number of sweets left in a box when 14 have been eaten is given by the equation

$n + 14 = 20$

Solve the equation to find the value of n.

 (ii) When calculating the time taken for a car to increase its speed from 20 km/h to 40 km/h, the following equation is produced

$40 = 20 + 4t$

Solve the equation to find the value of t.

[W]

7. A school decides to have a disco from 8 p.m. to midnight. The price of the tickets will be 20p. The costs are as follows:

     Disco and D.J., £25

     Hire of hall, £5 an hour

     200 cans of soft drinks at 15p each

     200 packets of crisps at 10p each

     Printing of tickets, £5

  (i) What is the total cost of putting on the disco?

 (ii) How many tickets must be sold to cover the cost?

(iii) If 400 tickets are sold, all the drinks are sold at 20p each and all the packets of crisps at 12p each, calculate the profit or loss the school finally makes.

[N]

8. A ladder of length 10 m rests with its lower end on horizontal ground and its upper end against a vertical wall. Calculate

 (a) the horizontal distance from the wall to the lower end of the ladder when it is inclined at an angle of 55° to the horizontal,

 (b) the angle that the ladder makes with the horizontal when the upper end is 8 m above the ground.

[S]

9.

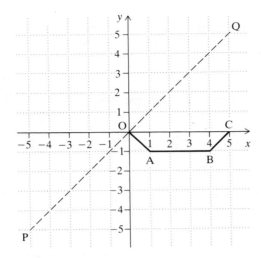

(a) Reflect the figure OABC in the x-axis and draw the image on the given diagram.
(b) The figure and its image are rotated through 90° about the origin in a clockwise direction. Draw the new image on the given diagram.
(c) The complete picture is then reflected in the mirror line PQ. Draw the final image on the same diagram.
(d) How many lines of symmetry has the final figure?
(e) What order of rotational symmetry has the final figure?
                                                                                                                    [L]

10. A swimming pool is of width 10 m and length 25 m. The depth of water in the pool increases uniformly from the shallow end, where the depth is 1.5 m to the deep end, where the depth is 2.5 m.
(a) Calculate the volume of water in the pool.
(b) This water is emptied into a cylindrical tank of radius 3.5 m. Taking π as $3\frac{1}{7}$, calculate the depth of water in the tank.
                                                                                                                    [L]

11. The diagram shows a sketch of the net of a pyramid. The base of the pyramid is shaded in the diagram.

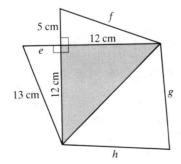

(a) Find the lengths of the lines marked e, f, g, h.
(b) Calculate the volume of the pyramid.
    [Volume of a pyramid $= \frac{1}{3}$ (area of base) × (vertical height).]
                                                                                                                    [M]

12. A group of children are queueing to select at random either an apple or an orange from a bag. Initially there are 15 apples and 10 oranges in the bag. The first in the queue is Megan and the second is Huw. Find the probability:
  (i) that Megan selects an orange,
  (ii) that Huw selects an apple given that Megan took an apple from the bag,
  (iii) that both Megan and Huw select an apple.

[W]

Examination exercise 2

1. The tables show the rail fares for adults and part of a British Rail timetable for trains between Cambridge and Bury St. Edmunds.

Fares for *one* adult

Cambridge				
£1.00	Dullingham			
£1.20	40p	Newmarket		
£1.30	£1.00	60p	Kennett	
£2.00	£1.30	£1.20	80p	Bury St. Edmunds

Train times

Cambridge	11 20
Dullingham	11 37
Newmarket	11 43
Kennett	11 52
Bury St. Edmunds	12 06

(a) How much would it cost for four adults to travel from Dullingham to Bury St. Edmunds?
(b) How long does this journey take?

[M]

2. The sketch of a clock tower is shown.

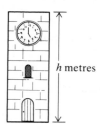

h metres

A model of the tower is made using a scale of 1 to 20.
(a) The minute hand on the tower clock is 40 cm long. What is the length of the minute hand on the model?
(b) The height of the model is 40 cm. What is the height *h*, in metres, of the clock tower?

[S]

3. The Compound Interest Table below shows how much £1 will amount to, in a given number of years, when invested at 10% per year.

No. of Years	1	2	3	4	5	6	7	8	9	10
Amount of £1 (to nearest penny)	£1.10	£1.21	£1.33	£1.46	£1.61	£1.77	£1.95	£2.14	£2.36	£2.59

Use the table to answer the following questions,
(a) How much will £100 amount to in 5 years?
(b) How much will £275 amount to in 7 years?
(c) How much, to the nearest £, must be invested to amount to £500 in 10 years?
(d) What is the least number of complete years for which a sum must be invested to double itself?

[L]

4. $1 + 3 = 2^2$.
$1 + 3 + 5 = 3^2$.

(a) $1 + 3 + 5 + 7 = x^2$. 　　(b) $1 + 3 + 5 + \ldots + n = 100$.
　Calculate x. 　　　　　　　　Calculate n

[L]

5. The diagram shows a lawn in the shape of a rectangle from which two semi-circles have been removed. The diameter of each semi-circle is 7 metres.

11 m

7 m

22 m

Taking π as $\frac{22}{7}$, calculate, in metres, the perimeter of the lawn.

[L]

6. This electricity bill is not complete.

NEA	
Northern Electricity Authority P.O. Box 6984 Manchester M49 2QQ Tel: 061 555 2718	Customer: G. J. Spinner 21 Silk Street Macclesfield SK27 3BJ

Ref: 0248-6879-5

METER READING on
07-11-84 　　　　　　　　　　　26819 units
METER READING on
04-02-85 　　　　　　　　　⬜ units
　ELECTRICITY USED 　　　　　1455 units
　　　1455 units at 5.44 pence per unit 　　　£ ⬜
　　　　　　　　　　Quarterly charge 　　　£ 6.27
　　　　　　　　　　TOTAL (now due) 　　　£ ⬜

(i) Write down the correct amount to be placed in each box.
(ii) In 1984, in what month was the meter read?

[N]

7. (a) The mean mass of 10 boys in a class is 56 kg.
      (i) Calculate the total mass of these 10 boys.
      (ii) Another boy, whose mass is 67 kg, joins the group. Calculate the mean mass of the 11 boys.
   (b) A group of 10 boys whose mean mass is 56 kg joins a group of 20 girls whose mean mass is 47 kg. Calculate the mean mass of the 30 children.

[M]

8. The shaded pieces are cut from a rectangular card as shown in Figure 1. The remaining piece of card is folded to make the *open* box as shown in Figure 2.

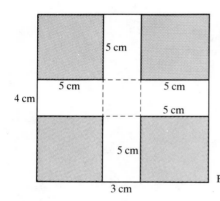

Figure 1

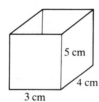

Figure 2

   (i) What was the area of the rectangular card?
   (ii) What is the area of the card used for the box?
   (iii) What is the volume of the box?

[N]

9. On graph paper, using the same scales, draw axes for x to vary from -6 to $+12$, and y to vary from -8 to $+8$.
   (a) Draw triangle ABC, where A is $(0, 4)$, B is $(2, 1)$ and C is $(5, 5)$.

   Transform ABC by the translation $\binom{6}{2}$ to $A_1B_1C_1$. Reflect $A_1B_1C_1$ in the x-axis to $A_2B_2C_2$.

   (b) On the same graph, draw triangle DEF, where D is $(-1, -3)$, E is $(2, -2)$ and F is $(4, -4)$. Reflect DEF in the y-axis to find $D_1E_1F_1$.

   Translate $D_1E_1F_1$ by the vector $\binom{0}{5}$ to $D_2E_2F_2$.

[L]

10. A metal ingot is in the form of a solid cylinder of length 7 cm and radius 3 cm.
    (a) Calculate the volume, in cm³, of the ingot.
    The ingot is to be melted down and used to make cylindrical coins of thickness 3 mm and radius 12 mm.
    (b) Calculate the volume, in mm³, of each coin.
    (c) Calculate the number of coins which can be made from the ingot, assuming that there is no wastage of metal.

[M]

11. AB is a straight shoreline of length 9 km. On a treasure map, a tall
tree T is 6.5 km from point A and angle TAB = 60°.
Using ruler and compasses only, construct a scale drawing of triangle
ABT.
The treasure X is equidistant from A and B, and also equidistant from
TA and TB. Showing all construction arcs clearly, construct two lines
on which X must lie. Hence find and mark the position of X.

[W]

12. The table below gives information about the TT Mountain Course races
for motorcycles. It gives the times taken to complete different numbers
of laps for average speeds of 100 mph, 104 mph, 106 mph and 108 mph.

Average speed in miles per hour (mph)	Time taken for			
	1 lap	2 laps	3 laps	4 laps
100	22 min 38 s	45 min 16 s	1 hr 7 min 54 s	1 hr 30 min 32 s
104	21 min 46 s	43 min 32 s		1 hr 27 min 4 s
106	21 min 21 s	42 min 42 s	1 hr 4 min 3 s	1 hr 25 min 24 s
108	20 min 58 s	41 min 56 s	1 hr 2 min 54 s	1 hr 23 min 52 s

(i) How long does it take to do two laps at an average speed of
104 mph?
(ii) Write down the missing entry in the table.
(iii) How long would it take to do six laps at 106 mph?
(iv) Why do the times in each column get less as you go down the
table?
(v) A motorcyclist averaging 100 mph started at exactly 9.45 a.m.
At what time did he finish the first lap?

[N]

Examination exercise 3

1.

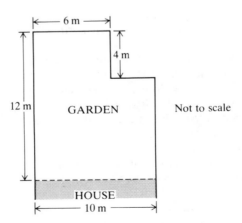

The diagram shows the plan of part of a house and all of its garden.
(a) Find the total length of the sides of the garden shown by solid lines.
(b) How many fence sections, each 2 m long, will be needed to fence
the sides of the garden?

[M]

2.

Basic holiday price in £'s per person — Gatwick departures												
Departures between	26 March 27 April		28 April 18 May		19 May 15 June		16 June 13 July		14 July 31 Aug.		1 Sep. 28 Oct.	
Number of nights	7	14	7	14	7	14	7	14	7	14	7	14
Hotel ESPLANADE	218	353	222	360	226	367	231	374	235	380	200	320
Hotel ATLANTIS	152	223	159	236	168	253	174	260	178	291	140	210
Hotel CALYPSO	139	195	150	206	153	219	156	226	162	233	120	181

Addition for Heathrow departure £24 per person.
Addition for balcony and sea view, £1.50 per person per night.
Addition for insurance cover £3.75 per person.

Using the above table, a man reserved a 14 night holiday for himself and family of three (four persons altogether), at the Hotel Atlantis, for the period from 22nd August to 5th September. He wished to fly from Heathrow Airport and to have accommodation with balcony and sea view for himself and his family. Insurance cover was required for each person. Calculate the total cost of the holiday for the man and his family.

[W]

3. The following are the first six numbers, written in order of size, of a pattern.
4, 13, 28, 49, 76, 109.
(a) Which of these numbers are:
   (i) odd numbers,   (ii) square numbers,   (iii) prime numbers?
(b) The difference between the first and second numbers, that is 13–4, is 9; between the second and the third it is 15, between the third and the fourth it is 21. Work out the difference between
   (i) the fourth and the fifth,   (ii) the fifth and the sixth.
(c) By considering your answers in (b), find the seventh and eighth numbers of the pattern.
   Explain how you reached this decision.
(d) Use the method you have described to write down the next two terms in the following pattern.
   1, 4, 12, 25, 43, 66, —, —.

[S]

4. The diagram below, which is drawn to scale, shows a town B which is due east of town A.

Scale: 1 cm represents 5 km

  (i) Measure and record the length of AB.
 (ii) What is the distance between town A and town B?
(iii) Mark on the diagram the position of town C which is 25 km north of B.
 (iv) Using a protractor, measure and record the size of BÂC.
  (v) Write down the bearing of C from A.

[W]

5. (a) In 1975, an apprentice electrician's 'take home' pay was £30 per week. His weekly budget was as follows:

Rent, food, heat and light	£9
Clothes	£6
Entertainment	£8
Travel	£4
Savings and other items	£3

Draw a pie chart to represent his weekly budget.

(b) The pie chart represents the 'average family' budget in 1975. The 'average family's' net income in 1975 was £3,240.

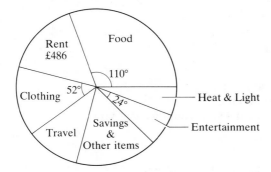

Calculate
  (i) how much was spent on food,
 (ii) what angle is represented by rent,
(iii) what percentage of the family's net income was spent on entertainment.

(c) By comparing the two pie charts, comment briefly on the major differences between the 'average family' budget and the apprentice's budget.

[S]

6. A cookery book gives the following instructions for cooking a leg of lamb.

     'Allow 40 minutes for each kilogram and 20 minutes extra.'
(a) Find the time, in minutes, required to cook a leg of mass 3 kg.
(b) Write a formula for the total cooking time, T minutes, for a leg of mass M kg.

[S]

7. (i) The total weight of a lorry, T tonnes, is related to its load, L tonnes, by the following formula
$$T = 20 + 2L$$
Calculate the value of T when $L = 7$.

(ii) The length, l, of the side of a square is related to the area, a, of the square by the following formula
$$l = \sqrt{a}$$
Calculate the value of l when $a = 81$.

[W]

8. The probability of a train arriving early at a station is $\frac{1}{10}$.
The probability of a train arriving late at a station is $\frac{2}{5}$.

(a) If 400 trains are expected at a station during the day, how many of them are likely to arrive at the correct time?

(b) What is the probability that both the trains arriving at the station from Exeter are late?

[S]

9. A cuboid measures 10 cm by 8 cm by 6 cm.

(a) On your graph sheet, using a scale of 1 cm to represent 2 cm, draw an accurate net which could be folded to make the cuboid.

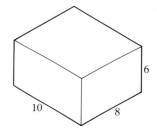

(b) (i) Find the area of the net on your graph paper.
   (ii) Find the total surface area of the cuboid.

(c) What is the minimum size rectangle of card you would need if you wanted to make two of the cuboids?

[S]

10. When Diane Wales attends meetings her car expenses worked out as follows.

For journeys of 50 miles or less.
$$\text{Amount} = £\,\frac{24N}{100}.$$

For journeys of more than 50 miles.
$$\text{Amount} = £\,12 + £\,\frac{(N - 50)12}{100}.$$

N is the number of miles travelled.

(i) How much will she be paid for a journey of 26 miles?

(ii) How much will she be paid for a journey of 75 miles?

(iii) How much will she be paid per mile for journeys of less than 50 miles?

[N]

11. Melanie Crisp entered for a sponsored walk in aid of Oxfam. This is her sponsorship form. She walked 13 miles.

AMBRIDGE YOUTH CLUB: SPONSORSHIP WALK for OXFAM: 31/8/85

Signature of sponsor	Amount per mile	Amount given
Mrs Crisp	5p	
Harry Crisp.	1p	
Auntie Jane & Uncle Bill	25p	
B. Kay	3p	
Ben Johnson	15 pence	
J. E. Dooley	60 pence	

GRAND TOTAL COLLECTED [   ]

Name of walker ...... *Melanie Crisp* ......

Distance walked .... 13 .... Signed ...... *B. T. Powell* ......

   (i) Complete the column 'Amount given' and fill in the box for the grand total that she collected.
  (ii) Melanie wanted to collect at least £20 for Oxfam. How many more miles would she have had to walk in order to do this?

[N]

12. The diagram below shows a straight section of motorway PQ, 900 m long, and a church C which is 700 m from P and 500 m from Q. B is a bridge over the motorway, midway between P and Q.

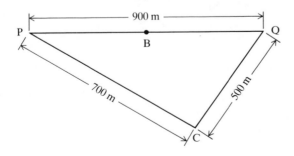

   (a) Using a scale of 1 cm representing 100 m, draw an accurate diagram, starting at the point P.
   (b) Find the angle PCQ, to the nearest degree.
   (c) Find the distance BC to the nearest 10 m.

[S]

Examination exercise 4

1. In December 1984, a factory employed 220 men, each man being paid
£130 per week.
   (a) Calculate the total weekly wage bill for the factory.
   (b) In January 1985, the work force of 220 was reduced by 10 per cent.
      Find the number of men employed at the factory after the
      reduction.
   (c) Also in January 1985, the weekly wage of £130 was increased by 10
      per cent. Find the new weekly wage.
   (d) Calculate the total weekly wage bill for the factory in January 1985.
   (e) Calculate the difference between the total weekly wage bills in
      December 1984 and January 1985.

[M]

2. A motorist travelled 800 miles during May, when the cost of petrol was
50 pence per litre. In June the cost of petrol increased by 10% and he
reduced his mileage for the month by 5%.
   (a) What was the cost, in pence per litre, of petrol in June?
   (b) How many miles did he travel in June?

[S]

3. (a) A gardener wishes to sow seeds on a circular lawn of radius 16
      metres. He uses 80 grams of seed per square metre of ground.
      Using $\pi = 3.142$, calculate
       (i) the area of the lawn to the nearest square metre,
      (ii) the mass of seed used to the nearest kilogram.
   (b) The figure ABCDEF is the uniform cross-section of a solid metal
      bar of length 2 metres. ABEF is a parallelogram and BCDE is a
      trapezium.

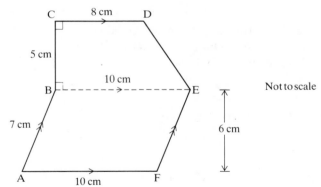

   Calculate
    (i) the area of the cross-section,
   (ii) the volume of the metal bar.

[W]

4. In triangle ABC, angle C = 90° and AC = 10 cm. The foot of the
perpendicular from C to AB is N and CN = 6 cm.

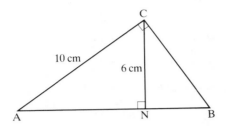

(a) Calculate the length of AN.
(b) Calculate the cosine of angle A.
(c) Calculate the length of AB.

[M]

5. The road and rail distances from Exe to Wye are both 144 km.
(a) The cost of a second class rail return ticket is £13.60 and the cost of
a first class rail return ticket is £20.40.
Find how much less a train passenger has to pay to travel, from Exe
to Wye and return, by second class rather than first class.
(b) A coach company charges a standard rate of 2p per km for each
passenger. A group of four people travel, from Exe to Wye and
return, by coach rather than by second class rail. How much less
does it cost the group?
(c) The rail fares increase by $12\frac{1}{2}\%$. Find the new price of a first class
return rail ticket.
(d)

Rail Timetable

Exe to Wye	Mondays to Fridays				
km					
0	Exe	04 38	10 18	13 40	16 18
64	Dee	05 46	11 26	14 48	17 26
144	Wye	06 53	12 33	15 55	18 33

(i) What time does the 13 40 train from Exe arrive at Wye?
(ii) Find the time taken for the journey from Exe to Wye.
(iii) Find the average speed of the 13 40 train from Exe to Wye.
(e) A coach arrived in Wye at 14 20 hours. It had travelled from Exe
at an average speed of 60 km/h.
(i) When did the coach leave Exe?
(ii) How much more time did the coach take compared with the
train?

[S]

6. Peter carried out a traffic survey of 80 cars passing the school gate, to note the number of persons in each car. The tally column has been filled in for the first 20 cars. The number of persons in the next 60 cars is given in this table.

```
2  3  4  2  1  1  5  2  2  3  3  4  3  2  1  5  4  4  1  2
5  1  1  2  1  3  1  4  2  1  5  6  5  4  1  2  3  2  2  3
1  4  1  2  5  4  1  2  3  4  1  3  4  2  1  1  3  2  2  1
```

(i) Complete the tally column for these 60 cars and hence fill in the frequency column for all 80 cars.

Number of persons	Tally	Frequency
1	JHT I	
2	JHT I	
3	III	
4	III	
5	II	
6		

(ii) Which number of persons per car occurred most frequently?

(iii) Find the mean number of persons per car in these 80 cars.

[N]

7. A factory cafeteria contains a vending machine which sells drinks. On a typical day:

> the machine starts half full,
> no drinks are sold before 9 a.m. and after 5 p.m.,
> drinks are sold at a slow rate throughout the day, except during the morning and lunch breaks (10.30–11 a.m. and 1–2 p.m.) when there is a greater demand.
> the machine is filled up just before the lunch break. (It takes about 10 minutes to fill.)

Sketch a graph showing how the number of drinks in the machine may vary from 8 a.m. to 6 p.m.

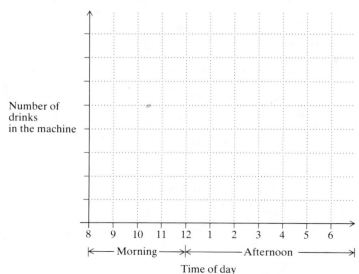

Number of drinks in the machine

8   9   10   11   12   1   2   3   4   5   6

|←—— Morning ——→|←———— Afternoon ————→|

Time of day

[N]

8.

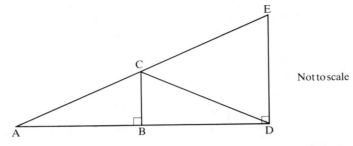

In the diagram above, triangle ADE is the image of triangle ABC after an enlargement, scale factor +2, using A as the centre of enlargement. Angles ABC and ADE are right angles.
(a) Write down the length of AE if AC = 7 cm.
(b) Write down the size of angle CED if angle ACB = 70°.
(c) Name an isosceles triangle in the diagram.
(d) Name two triangles in the diagram which are congruent to each other.

[M]

9. Construct triangle ABC in which AB = 10 cm, BC = 12 cm and AB̂C = 47°. Measure and record the length of AC, giving your answer correct to the nearest millimetre.

[W]

10. Having played 26 innings in a season, Emrys Hughes has a batting average of 46. Calculate the number of runs he must score in his 27th innings to increase his average to 48.

[W]

11. Mr Board took his wife and two children to Moscow to see the Olympic Games, and visited his travel agent to obtain the necessary information.
(a) The air timetable was as follows:

	Flight A	Flight B
London departure	11 05	13 50
Moscow arrival	14 35	17 15

   (i) How long did Flight A take?
   (ii) How long did Flight B take?
   (iii) Given that the distance from London to Moscow is 2520 km, calculate the average speed, in km/h, of Flight A.
(b) The cost of a package tour to Moscow was £250 per adult for a holiday, which consisted of travel and hotel only. A discount of 10% off this price was obtained for each child.
   (i) Calculate the actual price paid for each child,
   (ii) Calculate the total cost for the family of two adults and two children.
(c) Tickets for attending the Games cost 5 roubles per person per day. Mr Board purchased tickets for 12 days for the whole family.
   (i) Calculate the total cost, in roubles, of all the tickets.
   (ii) Given that there were 1.3 roubles for £1. Calculate, to the nearest pound, the cost of all the tickets.

[L]

12.

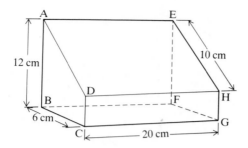

The figure represents a storage box in which
ADHE, ABFE, DCGH and BCGF are rectangles;
EH = 10 cm and CG = 20 cm;
ABCD is a trapezium with AB = 12 cm and BC = 6 cm;
∠ABC = ∠BCD = 90°.
The trapezium EFGH is identical in size and shape to the trapezium ABCD.
(a) Write down the lengths, in cm, of FG and AE.
(b) The rectangle DCGH has an area of 80 cm². Calculate
   (i) the length, in cm, of DC,
   (ii) the area, in cm², of the trapezium ABCD,
   (iii) the volume, in cm³, of this box.
   N is a point in AB such that ∠DNA = 90°.
(c) Write down the lengths of DN and NA.
   Hence, or otherwise, calculate, to the nearest degree, angle DAN.

[L]

Examination exercise 5

1. The cash price for double glazing the windows of Mr. Sharp's house was £3950. Mr. Sharp decided to pay by hire purchase.
(a) He paid a deposit of 20% of the cash price. Calculate the amount of the deposit.
(b) He also made 36 monthly payments of £118.50 each. Calculate the total of the 36 monthly payments.
(c) Calculate the total amount paid by Mr. Sharp for the double glazing.

[M]

2.

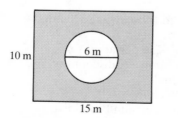

Not to scale

The diagram above represents a rectangular lawn, 15 m by 10 m, with a circular flower bed of diameter 6 m cut from it.
(a) Taking π as 3, calculate the area of the flower bed.
   (Area of circle = πr².)
(b) Calculate the area of lawn remaining. (It is shaded in the diagram.)

[M]

3.

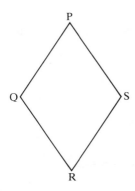

In the diagram, PQRS is a rhombus with each side of length 3 cm. A
point X lies inside the rhombus. It is given that X is less than 3 cm from
P and that the distance PX is greater than the distance RX.
Indicate clearly, by shading in the diagram, the region in which
X must lie.

[M]

4. A student asked 30 people arriving at a football ground how long, to
the nearest minute, it had taken them to reach the ground. The times
they gave (in minutes) are listed below.

$$\begin{array}{cccccccccc}
35 & 41 & 22 & 15 & 31 & 19 & 12 & 12 & 23 & 30 \\
30 & 38 & 36 & 24 & 14 & 20 & 20 & 16 & 15 & 22 \\
34 & 28 & 25 & 13 & 19 & 9 & 27 & 17 & 21 & 25
\end{array}$$

(a) (i) Copy and complete the following frequency table using the
intervals

Time taken in minutes (to nearest minute)	8–12	13–17	18–22	23–27	28–32	33–37	38–42
Number of people	3	5	7	6	4		

(ii) Draw a histogram to represent the information in the frequency
table.

(b) Of the 30 people questioned,
    6 paid £2 each to see the football match,
    8 paid £3 each,
    4 paid £4 each,
    10 paid £5 each and
    2 paid £6 each.
    (i) Calculate the total amount paid by these 30 people.
    (ii) Calculate the mean amount paid by these 30 people.

[M]

5. A motorist travelled from Carmarthen to Bristol, calling in at Swansea and Cardiff on the way. The reading on the car's 'distance meter' when starting the journey from Carmarthen was

0	7	9	8	4

The following route diagram shows the motorist's journey.

Using the route diagram (*which is not drawn to scale*)
  (i) write down the reading on the distance meter when the car arrived in Cardiff,
  (ii) find the distance from Cardiff to Bristol.

Given that the total distance from Carmarthen to Bristol is 195 km, and that on average the car used 1 litre of petrol for every 13 km travelled, calculate
  (iii) the number of litres of petrol used,
  (iv) the total cost of the petrol used for the journey if petrol costs 44p per litre.

[W]

6. A field is in the shape of a quadrilateral ABCD with AB = 80 m, BC = 70 m and CD = 110 m. Angle ABC = 80° and the angle BCD = 120°.
Using a scale of 1 cm to represent 10 m make an accurate scale drawing of the field.
  (i) Use your scale drawing to find the length of the side DA.
  (ii) A tree is at the point of intersection of the bisector of the angle CDA and the perpendicular bisector of the side BC. Using only ruler and compass construct and indicate the position of the tree.
  (iii) Find the distance of the tree from the corner B of the field.

[N]

7. Two bags contain coloured beads.
Bag A contains 3 blue beads and 1 red bead.
Bag B contains 3 blue beads and 3 red beads.
Two draws are made, at random in each case.
Draw 1. A bead is taken from Bag A and put in Bag B.
Draw 2. A bead is taken from Bag B.
Write the appropriate probabilities on the branches of the tree diagram.

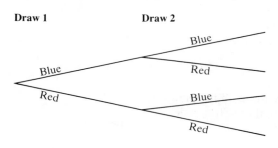

[N]

8. The diagram shows three posts A, B and C on a building site.

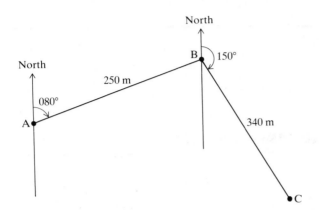

(a) Using the distances and bearings shown on the diagram and with a scale of 1 cm to represent 50 m, make a scale drawing to show the positions of A, B and C.

(b) (i) Join AC and measure its length to the nearest millimetre.
    (ii) What is the distance, on the building site, between the two posts A and C?

(c) (i) Measure and write down the size of angle BAC.
    (ii) What is the bearing of C from A?
    (iii) What is the bearing of A from C?

(d) By drawing further lines on your scale drawing, find how far the post C is East of the post A.

[S]

9. Mrs. Pinks drove her car from Sheffield to Cambridge University. The record of her journey in both directions is given below. The distance between the two cities is 208 kilometres.

Time	
06 30	Left Sheffield.
08 30	Car broke down 140 kilometres from Sheffield.
09 45	Car started again and the journey to Cambridge continued.
10 30	Arrived in Cambridge.
15 55	Left Cambridge for Sheffield.

(a) Calculate her average speed in kilometres per hour *before* the car broke down.

(b) Calculate the distance from Cambridge when the car broke down.

(c) Calculate the average speed between 06 30 and 10 30.

(d) Calculate the length of time in hours and minutes that she spent in Cambridge.

(e) On the return journey from Cambridge to Sheffield she averaged 64 km per hour. Calculate the time of arrival in Sheffield.

[M]

Think about it 3

Project 1   **A PATH AROUND THE LAWN**

Paving slabs 1 metre square are placed around a square lawn to form a path.
In Figure 1 the side of the lawn is 2 m and there are 12 slabs in the path.

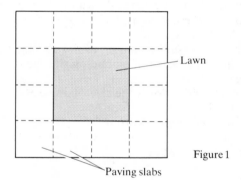

Figure 1

In Figure 2 the side of the lawn is 3 m and there are 16 slabs in the path.

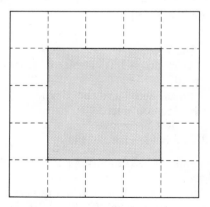

Figure 2

(a) Draw diagrams to show the paths in the following cases:
    (i) lawn 4 m × 4 m
    (ii) lawn 5 m × 5 m
    (iii) lawn 6 m × 6 m
    (iv) lawn 1 m × 1 m

(b) Copy and complete the table

Side of lawn s	number of slabs n
1 m	
2 m	12
3 m	16
4 m	
5 m	
6 m	

(c) How many slabs are needed for a lawn which is
  (i) 12 m square,
  (ii) 22 m square?
(d) What are the dimensions of a lawn where the path has
  (i) 64 slabs,
  (ii) 120 slabs?
(e) Can you find a formula connecting the side of the lawn s and the number of the slabs n?

Oblong lawns

Suppose the lawn is an oblong shape where the length is always 1 m more than the width w. In figure 3 the width is 2 m and there are 14 slabs.

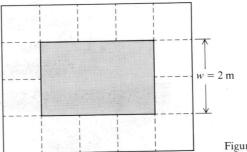

$w = 2$ m

Figure 3

(a) Drawn diagrams to show the paths in the following cases:
  (i) lawn 3 m by 4 m ($w = 3$)
  (ii) lawn 4 m by 5 m ($w = 4$)
  (iii) lawn 5 m by 6 m ($w = 5$)
  (iv) lawn 1 m by 2 m ($w = 1$)
(b) Draw a table of results for the width of the lawn w and the number of slabs n.
(c) Can you find a formula connecting w and n?
(d) Finally consider lawns where the length is always twice the width (1 m by 2 m, 2 m by 4 m, 3 m by 6 m etc).
  Draw diagrams and use the results to find a formula connecting the width of the lawn w and the number of slabs n.

Exercise A

1. When mixing sand and cement a workman puts three times as much sand as cement in the mixture. How much sand does he need for a mixture which weighs 120 kg?

2. Copy and complete the following bill

12 kg of sugar at 42p per kg	=	£
4 kg of potatoes at ...... per kg	=	£1.44
...... boxes of matches at 31p per box	=	£1.86
Total	=	£

3. A car travels at a steady speed of 44 miles per hour for 8 hours. How far does it go in this time?

4. An aircraft flies at a steady speed of 410 nautical miles per hour for 4 hours. How far does it go in this time?

5. A ship sails at a steady speed of 22 nautical miles per hour for $7\frac{1}{2}$ hours. How far does it go in this time?

6. A man bought 30 records at £4.20 each and a number of other records costing £6.80 each. In all he spent £296. How many of the more expensive records did he buy?

7. A train took 8 hours to travel 440 miles. What was the average speed of the train?

8. A lorry took 11 hours to travel 682 km. What was the average speed of the lorry?

9. A man took 3 hours to run a distance of $25\frac{1}{2}$ miles. What was his average speed?

10. Three girls are 144 cm, 147 cm and 153 cm in height.
    (a) What is their average height?
    When another girl joins them, the average height becomes 149 cm.
    (b) What is the height of the fourth girl?

Project 2   **DARTS: CAN YOU FINISH?**

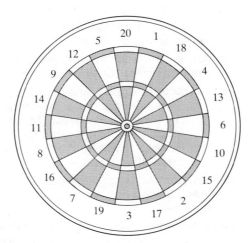

In the game of 501 in darts, players aim to score a total of 501 and they must finish on a double or a bull's eye (50).

For example, if a player has already scored 400 he has 101 left and he could finish 1, treble 20, double 20 (he has just three darts).

If he has 102 left he could finish treble 20, double 20, double 1. There are of course several other ways of finishing from 102.

Find ways of finishing with three darts for scores of 103, 104, 105, and so on up to 140.

What patterns do you notice?

What is the highest possible three-dart finish?

Exercise B

1. A large block of wood measures 10 cm by 10 cm by 20 cm. A small cube of side 4 cm is cut from the block. What volume of wood remains?

2. (a) Find 20% of £20
   (b) Find 5% of 2000 kg
   (c) Find 7% of 1400 m

3. (a) Copy the diagram of the regular hexagon below and draw in any lines of symmetry.
   (b) Calculate the size of the angle marked x.

4. A large wheel takes 30 s to turn once. How many rotations will it make in 1 hour?

5. Which is larger: 0.2^2 or ($\frac{1}{2}$ of 0.2)?

6. Sally is 13 years old and Dawn is 10. How many years ago was Sally twice as old as Dawn?

7. A bus travels 32 km on 8 litres of fuel. How many litres of fuel will it need to travel 100 km?

8. A grocer bought a crate of 40 tins of pears at 25p per tin.
(a) Find the total cost of the crate of pears.
(b) He wishes to make a profit of 40% on his cost price. For how much must he sell each tin?
(c) He sold 30 tins at 32p, and the rest of the crate at 40p. How much profit did he make?

9. An aircrafts' flight started at 2150 on Friday and finished at 1020 on the following Saturday. How long was the journey in hours and minutes?

10. A woman drives a car at an average speed of 70 km/h and the car does an average of 25 km per litre of petrol. Petrol costs 43p per litre.
(a) How far does she drive in 5 hours?
(b) How much petrol does she use?
(c) How much does it cost in pounds?
(d) How much petrol would she need for a journey of 500 km?

Project 3   SLIDING AND HOPPING

Object: To swap the positions of the discs so that they end up the other way round (with a space in the middle).

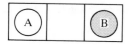

Rules: 1. A disc can be made to slide one square in either direction onto an empty square.
2. A disc can be made to hop over one adjacent disc so that it goes into an empty square.

Example: (a) Slide A one square to the right.

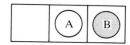

(b) B hops over A to the left.

(c) Slide A one square to the right.

We took 3 moves

1. What is the smallest number of moves needed for two discs of each colour?

2. Now try three discs of each colour.
   Can you complete the task in 15 moves?

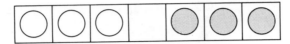

3. Now try four discs of each colour.
   Can you complete the task in 24 moves?

4. Results so far (hopefully!)
   For 1 disc we took 3 moves.
   For 2 discs we took 8 moves.
   For 3 discs we took 15 moves.
   For 4 discs we took 24 moves.
   Use these results to try to *predict* the minimum number of moves needed when five discs of each colour are used.
   Now confirm your prediction.

Exercise C

1. The area of a county is 6000 km². What volume of rain falls on the county during a day when there is 2 cm of rain? Give the answer in m³.

2. How many hours and minutes are there between:
   (a) 06 40 and 10 00
   (b) 11 30 and 14 50
   (c) 20 45 and 23 15
   (d) 08 55 and 14 00?

3. The basic rate of pay in a factory is £6 per hour for a 37 hour week. Overtime is paid at time and a half.
   (a) Calculate the total earnings of Mr Jones who worked the basic week.
   (b) Calculate the total earnings of Mr Green who worked 40 hours.
   (c) Calculate the number of hours overtime worked by Mr Bradshaw whose total earnings were £267.

4. Calculate the shaded area. Take $\pi = 3$

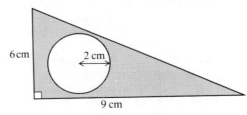

5. At 11 20 the mileometer of a car reads 97 460. At 14 20 the mileometer reads 97 715. What is the average speed of the car?

6. A map uses a scale of 1 to 100 000.
   (a) Calculate the actual length, in km, of a canal which is 5.4 cm long on the map.
   (b) A path is 600 m long. Calculate, in cm, the length this would be on the map.

7. Given the circumference C of a circle it is possible to estimate the area A by the following method:

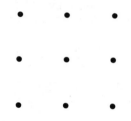

(a) Find A when $C = 6$ cm.
(b) Find A when $C = 18$ cm.
(c) Write down the formula involving A and C.

8. I think of a number. If I subtract 4 and then divide the result by 4 the answer is 3. What number was I thinking of?

9. Try to draw four straight lines which pass through all of the 9 points below, without taking your pen from the paper and without going over any line twice.

•   •   •

•   •   •

•   •   •

(Hint: The lines may go outside the pattern of dots).

10. Work out (a) $\frac{2}{3} + \frac{2}{5}$ (b) $\frac{2}{3} \times \frac{2}{5}$ (c) $\frac{2}{3} - \frac{2}{5}$

Project 4   **EXPERIMENTAL PROBABILITY**

1. Here is a mathematical probability game which has an interesting result.

Take the ace, two, three, four, . . ., ten of one suit from a pack of playing cards.

Shuffle the ten cards and then turn them over one by one and as you do so count 'one', 'two', 'three' and so on.
You 'win' if you turn over at least one card that corresponds to the number you call out as you deal it.

Before you try the experiment, what do you think is the probability of a 'win' in any one attempt: $\frac{1}{10}$; $\frac{1}{4}$; $\frac{1}{20}$?

Now work out the experimental probability of a 'win' by playing the game a large number of times.
Perhaps the whole class can play the game in pairs and then combine the results?

Count the number of trials (every time you start) and the number of 'wins'.

Calculate the experimental probability of a win as

$$p = \frac{\text{number of wins}}{\text{number of trials}}$$

2. Here is another experiment in probability where the result is perhaps even more surprising.

Two people each hold a shuffled pack of cards. Starting at the same time they each turn over the top card from their own pack. They continue to do this, always turning over the cards at the same time, until possibly they both turn over the same card. We will call this a 'success'. Once a 'success' has been achieved they can stop and start again, after shuffling the cards. If several pairs of people can perform this experiment many times we will be able to work out the experimental probability of a 'success' as follows:

$$\text{Experimental probability of a 'success'} = \frac{\text{number of successes}}{\text{number of trials}}$$

Teacher's note: In both experiments the theoretical probability of 'success' is given by the formula

$$p = 1 - \frac{1}{e} \text{ (where } e = 2.71828...)$$

Exercise D

1. Due to overproduction, the EEC destroyed 39 420 000 lb of tomatoes in 1985. Calculate the average weight of tomatoes destroyed
   (a) every day
   (b) every hour
2. A shopkeeper stocks two different sorts of gloves; he has 80 pairs of leather gloves and 60 pairs of woollen gloves.
   (a) He bought each pair of leather gloves for £6.20 and sold them for £8.50.
      (i) Calculate the total cost to the shopkeeper for the 80 pairs of leather gloves.
      (ii) Calculate the total amount of money received from the sale of all 80 pairs of gloves.
   (b) He bought the 60 pairs of woollen gloves for a total cost of £150 and sold them for a total of £210.
      (i) Find the total cost to the shopkeeper of the 140 pairs of gloves.
      (ii) Find the total amount of money received from the sale of all 140 pairs of gloves.
   (c) Calculate the total profit on the sale of all the gloves.

3. Write the following numbers correct to 2 decimal places:
(a) 1.752   (b) 0.3468   (c) 17.866
(d) 0.0753   (e) 0.0829   (f) 78.094

4. Use Pythagoras' theorem to find x:

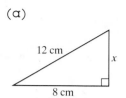
(a)

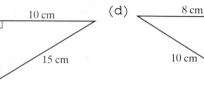
(b)   (c)   (d)

5. A boy spends $\frac{1}{8}$ of his money on sweets, $\frac{1}{4}$ of his money on magazines and the rest of his money on records. If he spends 80p on sweets calculate how much he spends on
(a) magazines,   (b) records.

6. (a) Copy the diagram of the regular pentagon below and draw in any lines of symmetry.
(b) Calculate the size of the angle marked x.

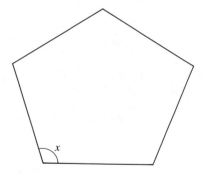

Project 5   **COUNT THE BLACK SQUARES**

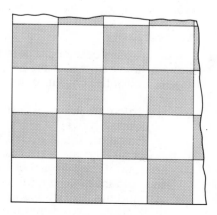

One corner of a variable-sized chess board is shown.
The board consists of black and white squares all 1 cm by 1 cm.

Drawn diagrams to answer the questions below and record the results in a table like this one.

Dimensions	Number of black squares.
6 cm × 8 cm	

Start with a white square in the bottom left-hand corner.

(a) How many black squares are there on a board with the following dimensions:

(i) 6 cm × 8 cm,   (ii) 8 cm × 4 cm,   (iii) 10 cm × 6 cm?

(b) How many black squares are there on a board with the following dimensions:

(i) 6 cm × 5 cm,   (ii) 8 cm × 7 cm,   (iii) 10 cm × 9 cm?

(c) How many black squares are there on a board with the following dimensions:

(i) 7 cm × 5 cm,   (ii) 5 cm × 3 cm,   (iii) 9 cm × 5 cm?

(d) Study the results for (a), (b) and (c) above and use them to predict (without drawing) the number of black squares on a board with the following dimensions:

(i) 13 cm × 12 cm,   (ii) 11 cm × 7 cm,

(iii) 12 cm × 8 cm,   (iv) 9 cm × 13 cm.

(e) Can you write down a rule (or rules) which enable you to calculate the number of black squares on a board of *any* size?

Project 6   THE MILK CRATE PROBLEM

You have 18 bottles to put into the crate below which has space for 24 bottles.

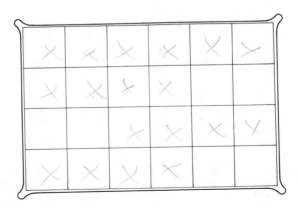

The only condition is that you have to put an *even* number of bottles into every row and every column. Good luck.

TABLE OF SINES

Angle in degrees	.0	.1	.2	.3	.4	.5	.6	.7	.8	.9
0	0.000	.002	.003	.005	.007	.009	.010	.012	.014	.016
1	0.017	.019	.021	.023	.024	.026	.028	.030	.031	.033
2	0.035	.037	.038	.040	.042	.044	.045	.047	.049	.051
3	0.052	.054	.056	.058	.059	.061	.063	.065	.066	.068
4	0.070	.071	.073	.075	.077	.078	.080	.082	.084	.085
5	0.087	.089	.091	.092	.094	.096	.098	.099	.101	.103
6	0.105	.106	.108	.110	.111	.113	.115	.117	.118	.120
7	0.122	.124	.125	.127	.129	.131	.132	.134	.136	.137
8	0.139	.141	.143	.144	.146	.148	.150	.151	.153	.155
9	0.156	.158	.160	.162	.163	.165	.167	.168	.170	.172
10	0.174	.175	.177	.179	.181	.182	.184	.186	.187	.189
11	0.191	.193	.194	.196	.198	.199	.201	.203	.204	.206
12	0.208	.210	.211	.213	.215	.216	.218	.220	.222	.223
13	0.225	.227	.228	.230	.232	.233	.235	.237	.239	.240
14	0.242	.244	.245	.247	.249	.250	.252	.254	.255	.257
15	0.259	.261	.262	.264	.266	.267	.269	.271	.272	.274
16	0.276	.277	.279	.281	.282	.284	.286	.287	.289	.291
17	0.292	.294	.296	.297	.299	.301	.302	.304	.306	.307
18	0.309	.311	.312	.314	.316	.317	.319	.321	.322	.324
19	0.326	.327	.329	.331	.332	.334	.335	.337	.339	.340
20	0.342	.344	.345	.347	.349	.350	.352	.353	.355	.357
21	0.358	.360	.362	.363	.365	.367	.368	.370	.371	.373
22	0.375	.376	.378	.379	.381	.383	.384	.386	.388	.389
23	0.391	.392	.394	.396	.397	.399	.400	.402	.404	.405
24	0.407	.408	.410	.412	.413	.415	.416	.418	.419	.421
25	0.423	.424	.426	.427	.429	.431	.432	.434	.435	.437
26	0.438	.440	.442	.443	.445	.446	.448	.449	.451	.452
27	0.454	.456	.457	.459	.460	.462	.463	.465	.466	.468
28	0.469	.471	.473	.474	.476	.477	.479	.480	.482	.483
29	0.485	.486	.488	.489	.491	.492	.494	.495	.497	.498
30	0.500	.502	.503	.505	.506	.508	.509	.511	.512	.514
31	0.515	.517	.518	.520	.521	.522	.524	.525	.527	.528
32	0.530	.531	.533	.534	.536	.537	.539	.540	.542	.543
33	0.545	.546	.548	.549	.550	.552	.553	.555	.556	.558
34	0.559	.561	.562	.564	.565	.566	.568	.569	.571	.572
35	0.574	.575	.576	.578	.579	.581	.582	.584	.585	.586
36	0.588	.589	.591	.592	.593	.595	.596	.598	.599	.600
37	0.602	.603	.605	.606	.607	.609	.610	.612	.613	.614
38	0.616	.617	.618	.620	.621	.623	.624	.625	.627	.628
39	0.629	.631	.632	.633	.635	.636	.637	.639	.640	.641
40	0.643	.644	.645	.647	.648	.649	.651	.652	.653	.655
41	0.656	.657	.659	.660	.661	.663	.664	.665	.667	.668
42	0.669	.670	.672	.673	.674	.676	.677	.678	.679	.681
43	0.682	.683	.685	.686	.687	.688	.690	.691	.692	.693
44	0.695	.696	.697	.698	.700	.701	.702	.703	.705	.706
45	0.707	.708	.710	.711	.712	.713	.714	.716	.717	.718

TABLE OF SINES – *continued*

Angle in degrees	.0	.1	.2	.3	.4	.5	.6	.7	.8	.9
45	0.707	.708	.710	.711	.712	.713	.714	.716	.717	.718
46	0.719	.721	.722	.723	.724	.725	.727	.728	.729	.730
47	0.731	.733	.734	.735	.736	.737	.738	.740	.741	.742
48	0.743	.744	.745	.747	.748	.749	.750	.751	.752	.754
49	0.755	.756	.757	.758	.759	.760	.762	.763	.764	.765
50	0.766	.767	.768	.769	.771	.772	.773	.774	.775	.776
51	0.777	.778	.779	.780	.782	.783	.784	.785	.786	.787
52	0.788	.789	.790	.791	.792	.793	.794	.795	.797	.798
53	0.799	.800	.801	.802	.803	.804	.805	.806	.807	.808
54	0.809	.810	.811	.812	.813	.814	.815	.816	.817	.818
55	0.819	.820	.821	.822	.823	.824	.825	.826	.827	.828
56	0.829	.830	.831	.832	.833	.834	.835	.836	.837	.838
57	0.839	.840	.841	.842	.842	.843	.844	.845	.846	.847
58	0.848	.849	.850	.851	.852	.853	.854	.854	.855	.856
59	0.857	.858	.859	.860	.861	.862	.863	.863	.864	.865
60	0.866	.867	.868	.869	.869	.870	.871	.872	.873	.874
61	0.875	.875	.876	.877	.878	.879	.880	.880	.881	.882
62	0.883	.884	.885	.885	.886	.887	.888	.889	.889	.890
63	0.891	.892	.893	.893	.894	.895	.896	.896	.897	.898
64	0.899	.900	.900	.901	.902	.903	.903	.904	.905	.906
65	0.906	.907	.908	.909	.909	.910	.911	.911	.912	.913
66	0.914	.914	.915	.916	.916	.917	.918	.918	.919	.920
67	0.921	.921	.922	.923	.923	.924	.925	.925	.926	.927
68	0.927	.928	.928	.929	.930	.930	.931	.932	.932	.933
69	0.934	.934	.935	.935	.936	.937	.937	.938	.938	.939
70	0.940	.940	.941	.941	.942	.943	.943	.944	.944	.945
71	0.946	.946	.947	.947	.948	.948	.949	.949	.950	.951
72	0.951	.952	.952	.953	.953	.954	.954	.955	.955	.956
73	0.956	.957	.957	.958	.958	.959	.959	.960	.960	.961
74	0.961	.962	.962	.963	.963	.964	.964	.965	.965	.965
75	0.966	.966	.967	.967	.968	.968	.969	.969	.969	.970
76	0.970	.971	.971	.972	.972	.972	.973	.973	.974	.974
77	0.974	.975	.975	.976	.976	.976	.977	.977	.977	.978
78	0.978	.979	.979	.979	.980	.980	.980	.981	.981	.981
79	0.982	.982	.982	.983	.983	.983	.984	.984	.984	.985
80	0.985	.985	.985	.986	.986	.986	.987	.987	.987	.987
81	0.988	.988	.988	.988	.989	.989	.989	.990	.990	.990
82	0.990	.991	.991	.991	.991	.991	.992	.992	.992	.992
83	0.993	.993	.993	.993	.993	.994	.994	.994	.994	.994
84	0.995	.995	.995	.995	.995	.995	.996	.996	.996	.996
85	0.996	.996	.996	.997	.997	.997	.997	.997	.997	.997
86	0.998	.998	.998	.998	.998	.998	.998	.998	.998	.999
87	0.999	.999	.999	.999	.999	.999	.999	.999	.999	.999
88	0.999	.999	1.000	1.000	1.000	1.000	1.000	1.000	1.000	1.000
89	1.000	1.000	1.000	1.000	1.000	1.000	1.000	1.000	1.000	1.000
90	1.000									

TABLE OF COSINES

Angle in degrees	.0	.1	.2	.3	.4	.5	.6	.7	.8	.9
0	1.000	1.000	1.000	1.000	1.000	1.000	1.000	1.000	1.000	1.000
1	1.000	1.000	1.000	1.000	1.000	1.000	1.000	1.000	1.000	0.999
2	0.999	.999	.999	.999	.999	.999	.999	.999	.999	.999
3	0.999	.999	.998	.998	.998	.998	.998	.998	.998	.998
4	0.998	.997	.997	.997	.997	.997	.997	.997	.996	.996
5	0.996	.996	.996	.996	.996	.995	.995	.995	.995	.995
6	0.995	.994	.994	.994	.994	.994	.993	.993	.993	.993
7	0.993	.992	.992	.992	.992	.991	.991	.991	.991	.991
8	0.990	.990	.990	.990	.989	.989	.989	.988	.988	.988
9	0.988	.987	.987	.987	.987	.986	.986	.986	.985	.985
10	0.985	.985	.984	.984	.984	.983	.983	.983	.982	.982
11	0.982	.981	.981	.981	.980	.980	.980	.979	.979	.979
12	0.978	.978	.977	.977	.977	.976	.976	.976	.975	.975
13	0.974	.974	.974	.973	.973	.972	.972	.972	.971	.971
14	0.970	.970	.969	.969	.969	.968	.968	.967	.967	.966
15	0.966	.965	.965	.965	.964	.964	.963	.963	.962	.962
16	0.961	.961	.960	.960	.959	.959	.958	.958	.957	.957
17	0.956	.956	.955	.955	.954	.954	.953	.953	.952	.952
18	0.951	.951	.950	.949	.949	.948	.948	.947	.947	.946
19	0.946	.945	.944	.944	.943	.943	.942	.941	.941	.940
20	0.940	.939	.938	.938	.937	.937	.936	.935	.935	.934
21	0.934	.933	.932	.932	.931	.930	.930	.929	.928	.928
22	0.927	.927	.926	.925	.925	.924	.923	.923	.922	.921
23	0.921	.920	.919	.918	.918	.917	.916	.916	.915	.914
24	0.914	.913	.912	.911	.911	.910	.909	.909	.908	.907
25	0.906	.906	.905	.904	.903	.903	.902	.901	.900	.900
26	0.899	.898	.897	.896	.896	.895	.894	.893	.893	.892
27	0.891	.890	.889	.889	.888	.887	.886	.885	.885	.884
28	0.883	.882	.881	.880	.880	.879	.878	.877	.876	.875
29	0.875	.874	.873	.872	.871	.870	.869	.869	.868	.867
30	0.866	.865	.864	.863	.863	.862	.861	.860	.859	.858
31	0.857	.856	.855	.854	.854	.853	.852	.851	.850	.849
32	0.848	.847	.846	.845	.844	.843	.842	.842	.841	.840
33	0.839	.838	.837	.836	.835	.834	.833	.832	.841	.840
34	0.829	.828	.827	.826	.825	.824	.823	.822	.831	.830
35	0.819	.818	.817	.816	.815	.814	.813	.812	.811	.810
36	0.809	.808	.807	.806	.805	.804	.803	.802	.801	.800
37	0.799	.798	.797	.795	.794	.793	.792	.791	.790	.789
38	0.788	.787	.786	.785	.784	.783	.782	.780	.779	.778
39	0.777	.776	.775	.774	.773	.772	.771	.769	.768	.767
40	0.766	.765	.764	.763	.762	.760	.759	.758	.757	.756
41	0.755	.754	.752	.751	.750	.749	.748	.747	.745	.744
42	0.743	.742	.741	.740	.738	.737	.736	.735	.734	.733
43	0.731	.730	.729	.728	.727	.725	.724	.723	.722	.721
44	0.719	.718	.717	.716	.714	.713	.712	.711	.710	.708
45	0.707	.706	.705	.703	.702	.701	.700	.698	.697	.696

TABLE OF COSINES – *continued*

Angle in degrees	.0	.1	.2	.3	.4	.5	.6	.7	.8	.9
45	0.707	.706	.705	.703	.702	.701	.700	.698	.697	.696
46	0.695	.693	.692	.691	.690	.688	.687	.686	.685	.683
47	0.682	.681	.679	.678	.677	.676	.674	.673	.672	.670
48	0.669	.668	.667	.665	.664	.663	.661	.660	.659	.657
49	0.656	.655	.653	.652	.651	.649	.648	.647	.645	.644
50	0.643	.641	.640	.639	.637	.636	.635	.633	.632	.631
51	0.629	.628	.627	.625	.624	.623	.621	.620	.618	.617
52	0.616	.614	.613	.612	.610	.609	.607	.606	.605	.603
53	0.602	.600	.599	.598	.596	.595	.593	.592	.591	.589
54	0.588	.586	.585	.584	.582	.581	.579	.578	.576	.575
55	0.574	.572	.571	.569	.568	.566	.565	.564	.562	.561
56	0.559	.558	.556	.555	.553	.552	.550	.549	.548	.546
57	0.545	.543	.542	.540	.539	.537	.536	.534	.533	.531
58	0.530	.528	.527	.525	.524	.522	.521	.520	.518	.517
59	0.515	.514	.512	.511	.509	.508	.506	.505	.503	.502
60	0.500	.498	.497	.495	.494	.492	.491	.489	.488	.486
61	0.485	.483	.482	.480	.479	.477	.476	.474	.473	.471
62	0.469	.468	.466	.465	.463	.462	.460	.459	.457	.456
63	0.454	.452	.451	.449	.448	.446	.445	.443	.442	.440
64	0.438	.437	.435	.434	.432	.431	.429	.427	.426	.424
65	0.423	.421	.419	.418	.416	.415	.413	.412	.410	.408
66	0.407	.405	.404	.402	.400	.399	.397	.396	.394	.392
67	0.391	.389	.388	.386	.384	.383	.381	.379	.378	.376
68	0.375	.373	.371	.370	.368	.367	.365	.363	.362	.360
69	0.358	.357	.355	.353	.352	.350	.349	.347	.345	.344
70	0.342	.340	.339	.337	.335	.334	.332	.331	.329	.327
71	0.326	.324	.322	.321	.319	.317	.316	.314	.312	.311
72	0.309	.307	.306	.304	.302	.301	.299	.297	.296	.294
73	0.292	.291	.289	.287	.286	.284	.282	.281	.279	.277
74	0.276	.274	.272	.271	.269	.267	.266	.264	.262	.261
75	0.259	.257	.255	.254	.252	.250	.249	.247	.245	.244
76	0.242	.240	.239	.237	.235	.233	.232	.230	.228	.227
77	0.225	.223	.222	.220	.218	.216	.215	.213	.211	.210
78	0.208	.206	.204	.203	.201	.199	.198	.196	.194	.193
79	0.191	.189	.187	.186	.184	.182	.181	.179	.177	.175
80	0.174	.172	.170	.168	.167	.165	.163	.162	.160	.158
81	0.156	.155	.153	.151	.150	.148	.146	.144	.143	.141
82	0.139	.137	.136	.134	.132	.131	.129	.127	.125	.124
83	0.122	.120	.118	.117	.115	.113	.111	.110	.108	.106
84	0.105	.103	.101	.099	.098	.096	.094	.092	.091	.089
85	0.087	.085	.084	.082	.080	.078	.077	.075	.073	.071
86	0.070	.068	.066	.065	.063	.061	.059	.058	.056	.054
87	0.052	.051	.049	.047	.045	.044	.042	.040	.038	.037
88	0.035	.033	.031	.030	.028	.026	.024	.023	.021	.019
89	0.017	.016	.014	.012	.010	.009	.007	.005	.003	.002
90	0.000									

TABLE OF TANGENTS

Angle in degrees	.0	.1	.2	.3	.4	.5	.6	.7	.8	.9
0	0.000	.002	.003	.005	.007	.000	.010	.012	.014	.016
1	0.017	.019	.021	.023	.024	.026	.028	.030	.031	.033
2	0.035	.037	.038	.040	.042	.044	.045	.047	.049	.051
3	0.052	.054	.056	.058	.059	.061	.063	.065	.066	.068
4	0.070	.072	.073	.075	.077	.079	.080	.082	.084	.086
5	0.087	.089	.091	.093	.095	.096	.098	.100	.102	.103
6	0.105	.107	.109	.110	.112	.114	.116	.117	.119	.121
7	0.123	.125	.126	.128	.130	.132	.133	.135	.137	.139
8	0.141	.142	.144	.146	.148	.149	.151	.153	.155	.157
9	0.158	.160	.162	.164	.166	.167	.169	.171	.173	.175
10	0.176	.178	.180	.182	.184	.185	.187	.189	.191	.193
11	0.194	.196	.198	.200	.202	.203	.205	.207	.209	.211
12	0.213	.214	.216	.218	.220	.222	.224	.225	.227	.229
13	0.231	.233	.235	.236	.238	.240	.242	.244	.246	.247
14	0.249	.251	.253	.255	.257	.259	.260	.262	.264	.266
15	0.268	.270	.272	.274	.275	.277	.279	.281	.283	.285
16	0.287	.289	.291	.292	.294	.296	.298	.300	.302	.304
17	0.306	.308	.310	.311	.313	.315	.317	.319	.321	.323
18	0.325	.327	.329	.331	.333	.335	.337	.338	.340	.342
19	0.344	.346	.348	.350	.352	.354	.356	.358	.360	.362
20	0.364	.366	.368	.370	.372	.374	.376	.378	.380	.382
21	0.384	.386	.388	.390	.392	.394	.396	.398	.400	.402
22	0.404	.406	.408	.410	.412	.414	.416	.418	.420	.422
23	0.424	.427	.429	.431	.433	.435	.437	.439	.441	.443
24	0.445	.447	.449	.452	.454	.456	.458	.460	.462	.464
25	0.466	.468	.471	.473	.475	.477	.479	.481	.483	.486
26	0.488	.490	.492	.494	.496	.499	.501	.503	.505	.507
27	0.510	.512	.514	.516	.518	.521	.523	.525	.527	.529
28	0.532	.534	.536	.538	.541	.543	.545	.547	.550	.552
29	0.554	.557	.559	.561	.563	.566	.568	.570	.573	.575
30	0.577	.580	.582	.584	.587	.589	.591	.594	.596	.598
31	0.601	.603	.606	.608	.610	.613	.615	.618	.620	.622
32	0.625	.627	.630	.632	.635	.637	.640	.642	.644	.647
33	0.649	.652	.654	.657	.659	.662	.664	.667	.669	.672
34	0.675	.677	.680	.682	.685	.687	.690	.692	.695	.698
35	0.700	.703	.705	.708	.711	.713	.716	.719	.721	.724
36	0.727	.729	.732	.735	.737	.740	.743	.745	.748	.751
37	0.754	.756	.759	.762	.765	.767	.770	.773	.776	.778
38	0.781	.784	.787	.790	.793	.795	.798	.801	.804	.807
39	0.810	.813	.816	.818	.821	.824	.827	.830	.833	.836
40	0.839	.842	.845	.848	.851	.854	.857	.860	.863	.866
41	0.869	.872	.875	.879	.882	.885	.888	.891	.894	.897
42	0.900	.904	.907	.910	.913	.916	.920	.923	.926	.929
43	0.933	.936	.939	.942	.946	.949	.952	.956	.959	.962
44	0.966	.969	.972	.976	.979	.983	.986	.990	.993	.997
45	1.00	1.00	1.01	1.01	1.01	1.02	1.02	1.02	1.03	1.03

TABLE OF TANGENTS – *continued*

Angle in degrees	.0	.1	.2	.3	.4	.5	.6	.7	.8	.9
45	1.00	1.00	1.01	1.01	1.01	1.02	1.02	1.02	1.03	1.03
46	1.04	1.04	1.04	1.05	1.05	1.05	1.06	1.06	1.06	1.07
47	1.07	1.08	1.08	1.08	1.09	1.09	1.10	1.10	1.10	1.11
48	1.11	1.11	1.12	1.12	1.13	1.13	1.13	1.14	1.14	1.15
49	1.15	1.15	1.16	1.16	1.17	1.17	1.17	1.18	1.18	1.19
50	1.19	1.20	1.20	1.20	1.21	1.21	1.22	1.22	1.23	1.23
51	1.23	1.24	1.24	1.25	1.25	1.26	1.26	1.27	1.27	1.28
52	1.28	1.28	1.29	1.29	1.30	1.30	1.31	1.31	1.32	1.32
53	1.33	1.33	1.34	1.34	1.35	1.35	1.36	1.36	1.37	1.37
54	1.38	1.38	1.39	1.39	1.40	1.40	1.41	1.41	1.42	1.42
55	1.43	1.43	1.44	1.44	1.45	1.46	1.46	1.47	1.47	1.48
56	1.48	1.49	1.49	1.50	1.51	1.51	1.52	1.52	1.53	1.53
57	1.54	1.55	1.55	1.56	1.56	1.57	1.58	1.58	1.59	1.59
58	1.60	1.61	1.61	1.62	1.63	1.63	1.64	1.64	1.65	1.66
59	1.66	1.67	1.68	1.68	1.69	1.70	1.70	1.71	1.72	1.73
60	1.73	1.74	1.75	1.75	1.76	1.77	1.77	1.78	1.79	1.80
61	1.80	1.81	1.82	1.83	1.83	1.84	1.85	1.86	1.86	1.87
62	1.88	1.89	1.90	1.90	1.91	1.92	1.93	1.94	1.95	1.95
63	1.96	1.97	1.98	1.99	2.00	2.01	2.01	2.02	2.03	2.04
64	2.05	2.06	2.07	2.08	2.09	2.10	2.11	2.12	2.13	2.13
65	2.14	2.15	2.16	2.17	2.18	2.19	2.20	2.21	2.23	2.24
66	2.25	2.26	2.27	2.28	2.29	2.30	2.31	2.32	2.33	2.34
67	2.36	2.37	2.38	2.39	2.40	2.41	2.43	2.44	2.45	2.46
68	2.48	2.49	2.50	2.51	2.53	2.54	2.55	2.56	2.58	2.59
69	2.61	2.62	2.63	2.65	2.66	2.67	2.69	2.70	2.72	2.73
70	2.75	2.76	2.78	2.79	2.81	2.82	2.84	2.86	2.87	2.89
71	2.90	2.92	2.94	2.95	2.97	2.99	3.01	3.02	3.04	3.06
72	3.08	3.10	3.11	3.13	3.15	3.17	3.19	3.21	3.23	3.25
73	3.27	3.29	3.31	3.33	3.35	3.38	3.40	3.42	3.44	3.46
74	3.49	3.51	3.53	3.56	3.58	3.61	3.63	3.66	3.68	3.71
75	3.73	3.76	3.78	3.81	3.84	3.87	3.89	3.92	3.95	3.98
76	4.01	4.04	4.07	4.10	4.13	4.17	4.20	4.23	4.26	4.30
77	4.33	4.37	4.40	4.44	4.47	4.51	4.55	4.59	4.63	4.66
78	4.70	4.75	4.79	4.83	4.87	4.92	4.96	5.00	5.05	5.10
79	5.14	5.19	5.24	5.29	5.34	5.40	5.45	5.50	5.56	5.61
80	5.67	5.73	5.79	5.85	5.91	5.98	6.04	6.11	6.17	6.24
81	6.31	6.39	6.46	6.54	6.61	6.69	6.77	6.85	6.94	7.03
82	7.12	7.21	7.30	7.40	7.49	7.60	7.70	7.81	7.92	8.03
83	8.14	8.26	8.39	8.51	8.64	8.78	8.92	9.06	9.21	9.36
84	9.51	9.68	9.84	10.0	10.2	10.4	10.6	10.8	11.0	11.2
85	11.4	11.7	11.9	12.2	12.4	12.7	13.0	13.3	13.6	14.0
86	14.3	14.7	15.1	15.5	15.9	16.3	16.8	17.3	17.9	18.5
87	19.1	19.7	20.4	21.2	22.0	22.9	23.9	24.9	26.0	27.3
88	28.6	30.1	31.8	33.7	35.8	38.2	40.9	44.1	47.7	52.1
89	57.3	63.7	71.6	81.8	95.5	115	143	191	286	573